Who Are We, Really?

The Truth About Why We Think and Act the Way We Do

ROBERT WIEDEMEYER

Dendrax Publishing
Brunswick, Georgia
USA

WHO ARE WE, REALLY?
The Truth About Why We Think And Act The Way We Do
By Robert Wiedemeyer

Published by:
Dendrax Publishing
100 Newman Drive
Brunswick, GA, 31520, USA

ISBN 0-9647407-8-8

Library of Congress Control Number: 2006920103

Publisher's Cataloging-in-Publication
(Provided by Quality Books, Inc.)

Wiedemeyer, Robert.
    Who are we, really? : the truth about why we think and act the way we do / Robert Wiedemeyer.
    p. cm.
    Includes bibliographical references and index.
    LCCN 2006920103
    ISBN 0-9647407-8-8

    1. Neurosciences--Philosophy. 2. Mind and body--Philosophy. 3. Act (Philosophy) 4. Cognition.
I. Title.

QP356.W35 2006   612.8'2
                        QBI06-600007

Comments and questions about any of the information presented in this book will be forwarded to the author for response, if mailed to: Robert Wiedemeyer , c/o Dendrax Publishing, 100 Newman Drive, Brunswick, GA, 31520.

*Dedicated
to those who know,
but know not that they know,
for they shall be exploited*

ALSO BY ROBERT WIEDEMEYER

*It's Not a Tumor — The Patient's Guide to Common
Neurological Problems*

TABLE OF CONTENTS

PART II

INTRODUCTION

In 1996, my first book, *It's Not A Tumor – The Patient's Guide To Common Neurological Problems,* was published. It was written after several years of caring for patients with neurological diseases in my profession as a neurologist. About the same time the book was released, I began realizing that I had spent the majority of my adult life dealing with questions concerning the diagnosis and treatment of brain diseases, and yet there were important questions of a different sort related to the brain that my training and experience had never addressed. Questions like, "How long does the present last? – "Can the brain be aware of itself?" – "Do we really have free will?" – "How do we know what's real?" began to bother me. I knew there had to be explainable answers for these types of questions and I knew the answers must necessarily involve the brain. I also knew that if I didn't try to find the answers, I would forever feel that I had overlooked one of the most fascinating parts of the puzzle that is the brain. I began researching in earnest the answers to these more philosophically oriented questions involving the brain. My goal was to find provable and definable answers that could finally put the constant debating about these types of questions to rest.

When I began researching the subject matter that eventually became this book, I quickly discovered that if I was going to investigate how the brain worked, beyond the mechanics ordinarily used to identify and treat neurological problems, I would need to investigate areas of research that were not usually associated with brain functioning. In order to finally determine the answers to the "deeper" questions about the brain, including those mentioned above, I found that it would be necessary to investigate and relate subjects like logic, time, reality, quantum theory, and relativity to how the brain functions. This required researching information in the fields of philosophy, theoretical physics, language, math, neuroscience, psychology, sociology, and anthropology, with the thought being that there would be ample information relating these fields to my area of interest. What I found was that researchers tend to specialize in one highly focused area of their specific field of expertise and they don't pay too much attention to what is being investigated in similar fields. The result is that there is a lot of highly specific and valuable information available, but not very much information that relates one field to another. After sifting through a vast amount of information, especially in the specialized journals of the various fields mentioned above, then cross-referencing all of it to suit my interests, I frequently discovered answers to age-old questions that sometimes caused chills to run down my spine when I realized how novel and exciting these discoveries were. For instance, you may have read about the long-running controversy involving free will versus pre-destiny. After correlating information obtained from appropriate areas of theoretical physics, philosophy, and math, it was surprisingly easy to prove that free will *must* exist, while pre-destiny cannot possibly exist. (See chapter on "choice".) Another example involves determining how long the "present" actually lasts. I discovered all types of philosophical and theoretical physics information on this subject, none of which was useful by itself. But once certain theoretical physics information was cross-referenced with neuroscience and philosophical information, the answer to this long-debated question seemed to jump out of my notes at me. (See chapter on "time".)

Recently I saw a quote by a physicist that read, "If the human brain was so simple that we could understand it, we would be so simple that we couldn't." It was narrow-minded statements like this that provoked my putting all the information I had collected into book form for others to read. I wrote this book because I felt there was too much shrugging of shoulders and unnecessary debating about topics that should, and do, have definite answers, once we know where to look for them. We have been debating and guessing about important things that concern the human condition for far too long. The answers to the hard questions *are* available, and I have tried to provide them in this book.

What should you expect to gain from reading this book? You can expect to learn enough about why people do what they do that it will change the way you look at life. For instance, when you watch the evening news on television and the newscaster relates a story about a crime that was committed, instead of wondering why anyone would do something like that, you will understand exactly what motivated the criminal to do what he did. If someone argues that a certain act is either moral or immoral, you will be armed with the necessary information to easily determine whether that act is moral, immoral, or neither. If someone prattles on about "time" being just an illusion, or that "free will" doesn't exist because everything is predetermined, you will know why these statements are in error.

Besides helping the reader to become more aware of why people think and act the way they do, this book also has two underlying messages. The first is that each person is his own center of the universe, figuratively speaking, because of how his brain works. In other words, you will see that nothing else matters for each of us except what's going on in our own brain and no one else's. All the questions about reality, existence, knowledge, consciousness, and so on are determined by each one of us within our own brain. The second underlying message is that every choice we make is *always* to benefit ourselves first, regardless of the circumstances. As you will see, this fact has some interesting implications and consequences.

The purpose of this book is not to tell you how to live your life, but to inform you of what goes on in our brain that makes us think and act the way we do. You will finally get definite answers to important questions about the human condition instead of the usual philosophic ramblings and witticisms.

For some readers, the information presented may seem depressing because it eliminates a lot of the "magic," or "mystique," associated with how the brain functions, replacing it instead with evidence and logic to show that the brain is simply a sophisticated machine, acting in a predictable way, just like the heart, lungs, and the rest of the organs in the body. Knowledge is power though, and knowing just what happens in our brain during various situations might dispel some of the anxiety that may be associated with those situations.

I have purposely not used any math or physics formulas in this book because math doesn't necessarily deal in what we experience as reality, so using math as an explanation for reality doesn't always make sense to our thought process, as you will discover when you read the chapter on math and the brain. I have also tried to refrain from using any technical terminology that would bog down a reader who is not science-oriented. For instance, I have used the term "wires" to refer to all the various types of neurons that make up the architecture of the brain because the term "wires" is more appropriate to visualizing what's going on, in this case. I've attempted to write the book so that any interested reader can understand it, whether his usual field of interest is philosophy, music, literature, physics, biology, or anything else.

There are two parts to this book. Part I deals more with the "nuts and bolts" of the subject matter, relating various disciplines like physics, language, math, time, relativity, and light to brain function, in order to show how the brain uses them in its normal functioning. These subjects fill in the more esoteric pieces of the puzzle that are usually missing in discussions about the human condition, even though they are essential to understanding what causes us to think and act the way we do. Part II draws upon the information presented in Part I to finally answer some of the most perplexing philosophic questions about life that have been debated for years.

Part I – The first chapter explains how we are able to know anything at all. That is, it explains how we perceive everything we are aware of through our five senses. Questions like, "Do we really 'see' anything?" or "If a tree falls in the forest and no one hears it, does it make a sound?" are answered in this section. What constitutes our existence is also explained, as well as what allows us to have thoughts and emotions. The long-standing question about why we need to sleep is finally answered here as well.

The second chapter explains why language is necessary for our thought processes to occur. The question, "What is life?" is finally answered using the information in this chapter. This chapter also explains why logic depends on who's making the choice and shows what it is about language that separates us from other animals. The next chapter on math and the brain explains why math does not always deal within the realm of our reality, even though it can be thought of as a special type of language. Some of what math entails would require more than the five senses we have in order to fully understand it.

The next four chapters deal with specialized areas of physics and how the brain deals with them. The chapter on physics explains how all matter can, and does, originate from nothing, how quantum physics puts our brain at the center of ultimately determining what exists, and why it is that the only thing we can really perceive is energy. The chapter on light explains why nothing can go faster than the speed of light, and that our brain's ability to perceive light figures prominently in this phenomenon. The chapter on time separates subjective time from objective time so that we can finally determine exactly what time is, how our brain deals with it, what the present, past, and future really mean, and finally dispel all the myths about time that have accumulated over many years. The exact length of time that constitutes "the present" is finally explained in this chapter. The chapter on relativity explains why it is that everything perceived or conceived depends on the frame of reference of the person who perceives or conceives it.

Part II – The chapter revisiting perception covers all the important concepts that have been debated for centuries. We finally have the information to understand the meanings and applications to the brain of consciousness, reality, conscience, rationalization, pain, altruism, behavior, judgment, learning, intelligence, beliefs, emotions, logic, and others, all of which are finally explained in this chapter.

The chapter on choice gives proof of why free will exists and pre-destiny cannot exist. It also explains what affects our choices as well as how we determine the value we place on human life.

The chapter on morals and ethics first explains why morals and ethics can only apply within, and to, a society and nowhere else. Once this is understood, it will be seen how easy it is to determine which acts are moral, which acts are immoral, and which acts don't apply to morality at all. The distinction between a "person" and a "human being" is also made, and the morality of abortion, suicide, and euthanasia is discussed.

Motivation is covered in the next chapter. Drives, emotions, and pain are the most important motivators for us. After the three basic drives of hunger, thirst, and preservation of body temperature are achieved, power is the most important drive. We will see just what people will do to satisfy these motivational forces.

The main point being conveyed in the chapter on sex and love is that sex and love are *not* related. Sex is a form of the drive for power, while love is an emotion. The implications of this are investigated.

Our need for religion is explained in the next chapter. It will be seen why the premise of religion is "belief," and that whether God exists or not is completely determined by each person in his own frame of reference.

The final chapter deals with living in a society, since that is how we all exist. The standard rules of society, mentioned first in the chapter on morals and ethics, are explained in more detail here, and "rights," which are also a product of society, are explained as well.

I began researching the information contained in this book because I wasn't satisfied with just knowing the mechanical structure and function of the brain. I felt that in order to really understand the brain's full capabilities, we also needed to know the answers to the deeper, more philosophic questions that necessarily involve the brain. I feel satisfied that this book contains the information needed to finally explain those previously unknown capabilities of the brain, and I feel confident that after reading the book, you will agree.

PART I

PERCEPTION – THE BASICS

Several years ago, while thumbing through the course descriptions in my college catalog, I came across a listing in the psychology section for a course entitled "Perception". It seemed like an appropriately lofty and esoteric subject, one that would almost certainly command adulation from my friends when I casually mentioned I was enrolled in it. But after reading the description of the course, I couldn't imagine anyone learning all the material that class promised to cover in one semester, so I passed on it and signed up for something else. Years later, I found that perception was not so much a lofty and esoteric subject, but rather, the basis of our entire fund of knowledge. Some people, myself included, would go so far as to say that perception defines existence.

Perception simply refers to any information our brain receives from one or more of our five senses. If you can't see it, hear it, touch it, taste it, or smell it, you can't perceive it. And if you can't perceive it, then it doesn't exist. That's all there is to it. I have seen perception described in print as "feelings," or as "concepts," but these descriptions of perception are in error.

You can't perceive feelings or concepts. Feelings and concepts arise from things taking place within the brain itself, not from information obtained outside the brain. You can't perceive a feeling, but you can perceive something that then evokes a certain feeling from within the brain. For instance, if you see a poor, starving child from a third world country on television, that scene may evoke a feeling of sympathy, but you can't see, hear, taste, touch, or smell sympathy for that child. Perception only refers to information we become aware of through our five senses. How the brain responds to that perceptual information after it receives it is another story, one that will be covered later in this chapter.

Before discussing each of the five senses individually, I would like to point out that you will begin to notice there is nothing magical or miraculous about any of them. They are fairly crude, as machines go, and they aren't nearly as exact in presenting information about the environment to our brains as we might think.

VISION

You have never actually "seen" anything. What your eyes record when you look at an object is light reflected from that object. If an object is incapable of bouncing incoming light waves off itself, you cannot visually be aware of its existence.

When a light wave reflected off an object reaches your eye, and travels to the retina at the back of the eye where the nerve cells capable of responding to incoming light waves are located, the energy contained in that light wave is transmitted to those nerve cells at the back of the eye, setting up an electric current in those nerve cells that eventually finds its way to the brain, where you become aware that an object is out there. So a light wave bounces off an object, enters the eye, is converted from light energy to an electric pulse in a nerve, travels to an area of the brain that records incoming nerve impulses, and suddenly you are aware that there's an object in front of you. Never did an actual, complete image of the object travel from the object to your brain. It almost seems like what used to occur on the old Star Trek shows when a person was disassembled into atoms, teleported to somewhere else, then reassembled back into a person again.

You have probably heard that there are two types of light receptors in the retina at the back of the eye. One type is for peripheral vision, which works better at night, or in reduced-light situations. The other type is for central vision, which works better in daylight, and is what we use for all of our detailed viewing. The nerve cells in the retina for central vision are more abundant and much closer together so that sharper images of objects can ultimately be sent to the brain for processing. This is because a beam of light entering the eye will stimulate more of these nerves than if the same beam of light strikes an area in the peripheral vision where the nerve cells are spaced farther apart. The greater abundance of nerve cells in the central vision can be compared to computer screens that have more pixels per square inch. The picture is much sharper and more detailed.

We think we're capable of seeing a wide expanse of scenery in detail at one time. For instance, if we go to a sporting event, such as a football game, we look in front of ourselves and see the twenty-two players moving on the field, the referees moving along with them, the five-yard lines drawn on the field, the crowd in the stands in front of us and across the field, and we see the grass on the playing field. But how much of this stuff are we actually seeing? The answer is – not much. When you look at an object, your central vision, the part that sees things in detail, and the part we use for nearly all our vision, is very small, relatively speaking. If you look at this letter "i" from as close or as far away as you wish, you cannot describe to anyone what the dot on the top and the vertical line beneath it look like at the same time, even though they're only a millimeter or so apart. In fact, if you concentrate on looking at just the dot itself, you can't be sure what the left side of the dot looks like while you're looking at the right side of the dot. The point of this is to show that our vision is very limited in its scope. As far as our vision is concerned, the brain spends most of its time filling in the gaps left by the "holes" in our vision. When we look at something, our central vision only sees a small part of it at any one instant, which means we really only perceive a very tiny aspect of whatever we're looking at, and our brain fills in the rest of the information, using memories of previous similar objects. Normal vision requires constant moving of the eyes to obtain continuous change of visual input to the brain. This results in lots of tiny pieces of the scenery we're viewing being sent to the brain. The brain then fills in any missing pieces from its memory stores in order to make what's being viewed more continuous instead of looking like a jigsaw puzzle with lots of pieces missing. How the brain does this will be discussed further in the section on memory.

HEARING

If a tree falls in the forest and nobody hears it, does it make a sound? Although philosophers have debated this question for centuries, the answer is that it does not make a sound. Sound is air compression at a frequency and intensity that can be, and is, perceived by someone. There can be no sound if there's no hearing apparatus to perceive it.

Hearing relies on the energy contained in compressions of the air that makes up our atmosphere. When something causes these "waves" of compression, and they travel away from the source, they may eventually reach a person's eardrum, causing it to vibrate back and forth at the same frequency and intensity as the original waves of compression. Inside the hearing apparatus in the inner ear, a long membrane is vibrated up and down by the pulsations of the eardrum. Because of the way this membrane is made, higher-pitched sounds cause one end to vibrate more, while lower-pitched sounds cause the other end to vibrate more. There are tiny nerves attached to this long membrane like teeth on a comb. Whichever part of the membrane vibrates in response to the incoming stimulus of the air compressions transmits the energy of the vibration to the specific nerves attached to that part of the membrane. When the nerves are stimulated in this way, they send an electronic impulse to the brain, and a person is then aware of the sound. How does the brain know whether the sound is high-pitched or low-pitched, since all the nerves that are attached to the various parts of the membrane in the inner ear are identical? The answer is that the part of the brain that deals with hearing is organized so that impulses from the nerves that are triggered by high-pitched sounds go to one area of the brain, while impulses triggered by low-pitched sounds go to another area of the brain. Like our sense of vision, our sense of hearing also depends on converting an external stimulus to simple electric impulses that travel through nerves to the brain. Ultimately, everything that makes us who we are can be traced back to an electric impulse moving around somewhere within the brain.

TOUCH

Although we usually associate the sense of touch with physically touching some object, it also includes many other sensations, such as vibration, itching, pain, the position of our bodies in space, temperature, and balance. These sensations are all cued by environmental influences on our bodies. They each have specialized receptors that react to the energy of movement of some external stimulus and convert that energy into an electric current that travels along a nerve attached to the specialized receptor. This electric current eventually travels to the brain, and we become aware of the presence of the external stimulus. The receptors for light touch are located in the outer surfaces of the skin and can be extremely sensitive to even the slightest touch of an object against the skin surface. Other touch receptors are located deeper in the skin and are more sensitive to pressure than to light touch. Pain receptors are located just about everywhere, and can be stimulated by extremes of most types of touch, including temperature, pressure, and itching. Just as we've seen with vision and hearing, and will see with taste and smell, touch also depends on some external energy source reaching a specialized receptor in the body, which then converts that energy into an electric current that travels to the brain, where we are made aware of it, and can either react to it or ignore it.

SMELL

There are two outgrowths from the brain itself that reach into the nasal area, one on the right and one on the left. Each of these looks like a hairbrush, with the outgrowths of the brain represented by the handle, and the many specialized receptors that project into the nasal cavity to pick up different smells represented by the bristles on the hairbrush. There are several million of these smell receptors projecting into the nasal area. If a tiny molecule that drifts into the nose and eventually comes into contact with one of these receptors has the correct conformation, enabling it to attach to one of the receptors like a key into a lock, it causes the receptor that it binds with to deform. This triggers the nerve attached to that receptor to send an electric impulse to the brain. The brain then interprets the electric impulse as a specific aroma. Different molecules that drift into the nose and are capable of binding to a receptor have different configurations that are recognized by the different specific receptors that can combine with those particular molecules. Since the nerve attached to each receptor goes to a different part of the brain, the brain recognizes each impulse as corresponding to a different molecule, or a different smell. If a molecule that drifts into the nose is not configured in such a way that it can combine with one of the specialized smell receptors in the nose, then it cannot cause a conformation change in any of the receptors, which does not result in an impulse being sent to the brain. The result is an inability to smell that molecule. For instance, when oxygen in the air enters the nose, it does not bind to any of the specialized smell receptors, so we can't "smell" oxygen. Some people can smell certain aromas that other people can't. This is simply because they have smell receptors that are capable of binding the molecules that make up that aroma, while someone else may not have those same receptors, and consequently, can't smell that particular aroma.

TASTE

Of the five senses, taste is probably the one that is least important. As much as we all like eating various tasty foods, we would derive almost no pleasure from the food we eat if we could not also smell it while we're eating it. Anyone who has lost the sense of smell with a bad cold and stuffy nose can attest to this. Their first complaint is that they can't "taste" their food. What they really mean to say is that they can't "smell" their food.

The sense of taste is confined to the tongue. There are specific areas in the front, sides, and back of the tongue for tasting four different types of food, including salty, bitter, sour, and sweet. These four types of taste are fairly crude, and are not very satisfactory for enjoying what we eat unless we associate them with the ability to smell our food at the same time.

As is becoming familiar, there are also special receptors on the tongue that are connected to nerves traveling to the brain. When these receptors come into contact with the appropriate bitter, sweet, salty, or sour food, they deform. This results in an impulse being sent to the brain along the nerve attached to that receptor.

In order for us to perceive anything, something has to move. That is, some sort of energy has to be transferred from whatever is being perceived to one of our specialized receptors for sensation, which then converts the energy of movement into an electrical impulse that travels along a nerve to the brain.

You might think we're very fortunate to have these five wonderful senses for perceiving everything around us, but those people who look at the glass as being half empty instead of half full might wonder whether we are being deprived in having only five senses to perceive things in our universe. What would happen if we had a sixth sense, or a seventh sense? The answer is that a lot would happen. We would be aware of the existence of more objects in the universe that we aren't aware of now. For instance, at the present time, astrophysicists are convinced that there must be a lot of extra "dark matter" in space because their calculations of the pull of gravity and the rate of expansion of the universe indicate that this is probably so. It is called dark matter because no one has been able to verify that it exists, and this is because no one has been able to perceive it. No one has been able to design a piece of equipment that makes it possible for us to either see it, hear it, touch it, smell it, or taste it. Now suppose we had a sixth sense that, in keeping with the basic design pattern of our original five senses, consisted of specialized receptors for detecting the energy of movement of some object; and suppose these particular specialized receptors could perceive something about dark matter that our current five senses cannot, such as some particular kind of energy it radiates that is not receivable by the receptors of our current five senses. If that were the case, we would be able to perceive dark matter just as easily with our sixth sense as we perceive the moon with our sense of vision.

Since it's hard to imagine what a sixth sense that is not available to us would be like, it might be easier to look at this scenario from a reverse perspective. Suppose we removed one of our five senses, such as our sense of vision, and we were left with just the other four senses. If none of us had ever seen anything, and then along came someone who was born with a genetic mutation that allowed him to see, how would he ever be able to explain to any of us who had never seen anything what the sense of vision was all about. Could he explain to us what a blue sky was? Could he even explain the difference between light and dark? The answer, of course, is that he couldn't. Now, taking this omission of senses a few more steps backward, suppose someone were born with none of the five senses. This person could not see, hear, smell, taste, or be aware of anything related to the sense of touch, which, as stated earlier, would include no sense of pain, temperature, position, vibration, and the others. His normal bodily functions would still proceed as usual, since one doesn't need to perceive these things for them to take place. He wouldn't be able to feel his heartbeat, though, and he wouldn't feel his lungs expand as he took a breath. If it were possible to feed him, he wouldn't even know he was eating, since he wouldn't feel the food in his mouth, wouldn't taste or smell it, nor would he feel it being swallowed. He wouldn't feel anything. He wouldn't even be aware of his own existence, because there would be no way for him to perceive this. Once we discuss memory and how the brain itself deals with information, including the concepts of time and especially relativity, this will become more clear. The important point here is that it just happened to turn out that at this stage of our evolution, we happen to be equipped with five senses, and there's no special significance to having five, rather than four or six senses. That just happens to be the way it is at the present time in our evolution, and it would be profoundly shortsighted and naive to think that with our five senses, we possess all the tools there are to perceive everything that exists in the universe.

MEMORY

The brain consists of several billion individual nerve cells, most of which are shaped like living electrical wires. In fact, I will refer to them as "wires" from now on, as this makes them easier to visualize. Each of these "wires" has branches that connect with thousands of other living wires in the brain, resulting in several trillion total connections between all these various living wires of the brain. The brain communicates with itself by way of all these connections.

I have occasionally read that we only use ten percent of our brain's capacity. This is completely false. We use one hundred percent of our brain, but not all at one instant. Over the course of several hours, for example, there is probably no part of the brain that doesn't have an electric current travel along its living wires. Although the brain consists of only two percent of our body mass, it consumes twenty-five percent of the energy we use. That should give some indication about how busy our brain is.

In spite of the complexity of the brain, there are only three things that it does. First, it receives incoming sensory information from our five senses. Second, it analyzes this incoming information by cross communicating with other parts of the brain.

Third, it can react to its analysis of incoming information by sending outgoing signals to muscles when necessary, causing them to move. In this section, we will look at what happens to incoming sensory information once it arrives in the brain.

The "Hardware" of Memory

Unlike a computer, which has special chips where memory is stored, there are no actual compartments for memory storage in the brain. In the brain, memory is carried in the way the living wires of the brain are connected to the other living wires of the brain. The more electrical impulses that travel along specific wires, the more branches and connections to other wires that particular wire grows. Out of all the signals that a wire receives from other wires, it conditions itself to only accept those from wires that are consistently active when it is active, and it ignores the rest. This is accomplished by making more, and stronger, connections to the appropriate wires. Along with that, the wires that are not used very much gradually are eliminated, akin to the "use it or lose it" philosophy. The reinforced connections that have become stronger, secondary to more use, serve as memories. Once the strong connections are made from using that wire over and over with the same information, then every time an electric impulse travels along that wire, a person suddenly becomes aware of the original information that first traveled down that wire when reinforcement of that information was being established – hence, a memory was made.

To better visualize how memories are laid out in the brain, you can think of the wires used for memory as being in the shape of a fork like the kind used for eating. The handle of the fork represents the incoming sensory information and the four tines represent the wires where the memory will be formed. If certain incoming information travels down the handle and then to the first and third tines of the fork, that could represent one memory. Then, if some different incoming sensory information travels down the same handle and travels to the first and fourth tines, or maybe all four tines at one time, these two different pathways could represent two different memories. Even with just four tines, it's easy to see that there are a large number of ways the various tines can be combined to receive sensory information via electrical impulses. Now, if a research scientist knew that these four tines were used to store memories, and he decided to dissect one of the tines out of the brain to study, say the fourth tine, what kind of memories would he find on that fourth tine? The answer is that he wouldn't find any. All he would find is a typical living wire of the brain that is used to carry electrical impulses. Memories are not actual "things" stored in the wires of the brain, but rather, they consist of the various, particular pathways that electric currents follow along a group of wires. For instance, if I see a red bicycle, the perception of that red bicycle may be represented in that instant as an electric impulse traveling down the first and third tines of our proverbial fork. Once that memory has been reinforced by permanently strengthening those tines so that they don't disappear later on from disuse, then every time an electric impulse travels down the first and third tines of that fork at the same time, I will become consciously aware of the red bicycle that caused the original impulse to travel down the first and third tines of the fork. When you think about the billions of "forks" contained in the brain, it is staggering how many different ways electrical impulses can be combined on them to form different memories. When you are trying to recall something from memory, what's actually going on in your brain is that the impulse generator in the brain begins sending electrical impulses down various "handles" of the forks, searching for the correct combination of "tines" that, when stimulated with the electric current, will make you consciously aware of the memory coded in that particular combination of tines. If a memory is used frequently, the tines that code for it have been reinforced by more frequent activity and are easier to find. If the particular memory you're searching for is not recalled very often, then it will not be reinforced very well and will be harder to find.

Memories can also transform our perceptions of the present. Using the example of the red bicycle I saw, which was coded for on the first and third tine of the fork, suppose I see that red bicycle again, and this time, when the perception of it reaches my brain and searches in memory for something to compare to in order to determine if I've ever seen that bicycle before – in other words, whether I have a memory for that red bicycle – it may accidentally send the impulse up the first and fourth tines, which may code for a blue bicycle, instead of the first and third tines, which code for the red bicycle. In that case, because the incoming information was erroneously matched to a wrong memory, then when I become consciously aware of the bicycle, I will become consciously aware of a blue bicycle I saw instead of a red one, since my memory system matched the incoming perception to the code for a blue bicycle. Remember that what we perceive is what our brain thinks we are perceiving. If incoming sensory information gets garbled somehow before we become consciously aware of it, then what we become aware of may not be the same as what we originally perceived.

It frequently occurs that as memories become old after several years, they become degraded and changed to the point where they are no longer the same memory that was coded for when something was first perceived. And the amazing thing is that the degraded memory can be just as vivid as the original memory, even though it is not the same. A person might be willing to swear that the Packard he owned fifty years ago was a green one, when, in fact, it was actually black. His memory no longer codes for a black Packard, and no amount of arguing can convince him otherwise because, no matter how much he tries to search his memory for a black Packard, that memory is no longer there.

Some scientists believe that every time a memory is recalled by sending an electrical impulse along the wires that code for that memory, it gets rewritten, or reconsolidated, from the act of having an electrical impulse travel along it. In this way, less important things associated with a complex memory can be slowly eliminated so that just the important part of the memory is retained with time. For instance, you may observe a car accident where a black car hits a white car. You may also notice that there were three people walking along the sidewalk, there was a tan dog standing by a building, and that it was cloudy. Several years later, the only thing you will probably remember is that two cars collided. The other information was not important, so it was gradually removed from your memory, avoiding a lot of clutter.

Children have many more wires than adults, even though their brains are physically smaller. As their brain is maturing, the wires are vastly over-produced, far in excess of what will eventually be needed as adults. This serves as a framework upon which all the memories the child will accumulate as he ages will be built. As he experiences life, certain of the wires will be used frequently, while others will not be used much at all. Those that are used frequently will grow more branches and will become more stable and permanent, forming memories, while those not being used much will gradually be eliminated. For example, the child has the framework required to learn any language that he could possibly experience. If he happens to live in the United States, he will probably learn English. The wires that are used while learning English will be reinforced and will grow many interconnecting branches for remembering the meaning of words and rules of grammar, while the wires he may have used to learn other languages along with English will gradually deteriorate and disappear. If he is exposed to seven or eight different languages, he has more than enough capacity in the framework for language to learn all seven or eight languages equally well. Once a child reaches the late teens and beyond, though, the ease with which additional languages can be learned diminishes, simply because the vast framework for permanently storing other potential languages in the brain has started to deteriorate and disappear from not being used, while the language learned is reinforced in the wires of the brain. This is why it is so much easier for a child to learn something that is completely new than for an adult to learn something completely new.

Things that occur together get stored as memories together. The brain doesn't sort perceptions out into individual packets of information and store them all separately. Whatever happens to come into the brain together from one or more of the five senses is dealt with, memory-wise, together in the brain. This makes more sense from a conservation-of-energy point of view, because chances are that if two things happen together, then they are likely to usually happen together. It wouldn't make much sense for the brain to have to store these as separate memories, and then have to seek them out from two different areas of the brain when trying to recall the complete perception. This fact is often used to advertisers' advantage. When trying to sell a car on television to a young potential buyer who is male, for example, they are sure to have an attractive young female sitting in the car, so that when the potential male buyer thinks about attractive females, he will also think about that brand of car at the same time.

Sometimes a perception that invokes fear is linked with a normally occurring perception. For instance, you may be in a bank waiting to cash a check when a bank robber walks in with a gun to rob the bank, and forces you to lie facedown on the floor. After that experience, you may feel very anxious whenever you walk into a bank because a single memory was formed consisting of both entering the bank and the bank robbery that took place at the same time.

Perceptions can also be manipulated to enhance analysis in the brain by selectively eliminating extraneous associated perceptions so that a single perception can be experienced by itself. For instance, if you have a delicious piece of pie ready to eat, and you're trying to read the newspaper and watch television at the same time that you start eating the pie, your brain is taking in information about what you're reading, watching, and eating, all at the same time. This means that not as much attention can be focused on how good the pie tastes. But if you close your eyes while you're eating the pie, filtering out any visual perceptual information, you will find that the flavor of the pie is much more intense, simply because the brain can devote more attention to the perceived information it's receiving about just the pie.

Comparing Old and New Memory

Memories are usually not stored exactly as the information contained in them was perceived. The essence of relationships, rather than all the details, is recorded. This is because it would serve no purpose to fill our brains up with useless details, from an evolutionary standpoint. It would make recalling memories a more tedious process as well, since there would be so many more memories to sift through before finding the one being sought out to compare to new perceptions being received.

When a perception occurs, the brain feeds the information to higher and higher levels of the neocortex, the six-layered part of the brain where memories are located, in search of a previous memory to compare it to. (Memories in the brain are arranged so that the lower levels of the six-layered cortex contain simpler memories that are more easily accessed, while the higher levels contain more complex memories that are a little more difficult, and more energy-consuming, to access.) Only after comparing the perception to memories already formed in the brain will the brain understand the input and know what to expect next, based on what has come next in the past when that type of perception was encountered. If there are no memories found in any of the six layers of the neocortex to compare it to that are similar to the perception, then a new memory will be formed. Ultimately, the goal of the incoming perception is to find a memory to relate to so that a prediction can be made that helps one to control his environment. In general, the brain doesn't want any surprises when it comes to dealing with incoming perceptual information, because the more surprises there are, the less certain one is about what will happen next, and the more uncertainty there is, the more anxiety there is. If, for instance, I go to a certain street corner to wait for a ride to work every morning, and an acquaintance picks me up at exactly eight o'clock each morning, I will probably become agitated and worried if, on a particular morning, I look at my watch while I'm waiting and notice it's approaching nine o'clock, and there's no sign of my ride. I may start wondering if he was involved in an accident, or whether he doesn't like me anymore and has decided not to pick me up. Then I may wonder if I'll get fired for coming in late to work, how I will support my family if I get fired, and so on.

The brain compares incoming perceptual information to stored memories to see what it needs to do next. If comparison is just as expected, where a sequence of events occurs similar to how our memory has recorded them to have occurred in the past, it reacts in the same way it usually does when that perception occurred in the past, or it does nothing. If comparison is different from what is expected, it pays much more attention, because it may have to make a decision to direct some action that it's never performed before. In this case, a new memory will be formed.

The more you know, the less you remember. This is because as you learn more, you have more memories that are similar to the new perceptual information coming into the brain. New memories are not made of these incoming perceptions, since they are similar enough to old memories that have already been formed in the past. If you take your child to the zoo, when you get home that night, your child will probably reiterate the entire experience to you, reminding you in detail about every animal he saw there. You will not remember the details of each animal as well as your child did because you already had memories of all those animals stored in your brain. When the incoming perceptions of those various animals entered your brain, they found similar memories to compare to, so no new memories were formed, including no new details of each of the animals. When the incoming perceptions of the animals entered the child's brain, and no old memories were there to compare the new perceptions to, then new memories were formed. By his recalling these new memories over and over, they gradually become permanent. Since they are new, they have much more detail than your older memories, which have reconsolidated and lost much of the details over the years. Although we do lose brain cells with old age, some of the "forgetfulness" associated with old age is also due to not receiving as much truly novel information. We've "seen it all before" in some similar fashion, so our brains don't bother to form new memories of a lot of the incoming perceptions.

When it comes to forming memories in the brain, there is no magical or deeply complicated process going on. What occurs is a simple act of comparing new perceptual information to old perceptual information by recalling the old when the new arrives. If a match is found, then the new is either taken lightly or completely forgotten. If a match is not found, then the new information is retained as a new memory. But if this new memory is not reinforced and made more permanent by repeated similar perceptions, it will gradually fade away from the memory areas of the brain after a period of time.

Consolidation of Memory

The brain doesn't remember exactly what is perceived through the senses. It remembers the important relationships of perceptions, independent of the details. So once a perception reaches the brain, the brain compares the incoming information to what's in memory, then chooses what parts of the perception are important enough to remember, and will let the rest fade away. In general, a perception that is repeated over and over is more likely to be remembered than those that occur infrequently, and it is not remembered exactly as it arrived at the brain. The brain consolidates it into just the important facts and disregards the rest of the perception. Later, if another perception that is very similar arrives at the brain, and is compared to the previous memory of it, only the salient parts of the incoming perception and of the memory of the previous perception of it are compared. If they are a close enough match, the brain will accept the incoming perception as a repeat of information it already contains in memory and will fill in the details to make the "story" of this incoming perception flow when it is being recalled at some future time. The continuous story being recalled later will probably not be identical to that latest perception that was received, but it will be close enough. You might wonder what good a memory is if it's not going to be recorded in the brain exactly as it occurred, so that when it is recalled, it will be an accurate account of what was perceived. The answer is that the important parts of the perception will be consolidated and remembered accurately. Only the unimportant parts will be disregarded and filled in later by the brain. As an example of this, let's say you happen to witness an auto accident between two cars, and you notice that the driver who was at fault quickly drove away, leaving a severely injured victim from the other car lying in the road. Your brain will immediately start making decisions about what are important facts to remember in this situation as lots and lots of incoming sensory perceptions arrive there. The brain might consider the escaping hit-and-run driver's appearance, make and color of car, and license plate number as important things to remember, but will not consider as important facts such things as the height of trees by the side of the road, the type of buildings that might be nearby, or the color of the clothes the injured person is wearing. Now how did you know that the license plate number of the escaping car was something to remember, while the height of trees by the road was not? The answer is because, as all of the visual perceptions of what you were witnessing reached your brain, they were quickly compared to the consolidated memories you had previously formed from perceptions pertaining to what one should remember at an accident, which you probably learned, or stored in memory, after hearing about it from someone else or reading it in a newspaper, for example. As all the perceptions of the moment of the accident were compared to memories in your brain for what should be noted at a hit-and-run accident, matches were found for license plate, characteristics of the escaping driver, and make of car, while no matches were found for height of trees by the road. Therefore, you zeroed in on the matches and forgot about the non-matches. This is the importance of consolidation of memories in the brain. If there were no consolidation of memories, and they were stored in memory just as perceived with all the details, then there would have been no matches found for what you should remember about a hit-and-run accident, and when the police came to ask you what you saw, you might tell them that there was a gas station across the street from the accident because, when all the various perceptions were coming into your brain at the time of the accident, there was no way for your brain to tell you what was important and what wasn't. There was nothing from memory with *all* the details that matched the incoming information. But with consolidation of memories, where just the important information is retained, it's a lot easier to find a match. This is somewhat akin to doing a web search on a computer. If you give just a few important details, you are much more likely to eventually find a match than if you give several details to match, including minutia that may not even be recorded in anyone's data base.

Not only does the brain consolidate perceptions to make them easier to match to new perceptions, but it also integrates memories from one sensory modality, such as vision, with another sensory modality, such as hearing. By doing this, the memories become less fragmented and easier to recall. For instance, if you hear a rattling sound and see the rattle snake that's making that sound at the same time, and form memories of both the sound and the visual perceptions that are integrated, then when you hear that characteristic rattling sound sometime in the future, the perception of the rattling, when it matches to the memory in your brain for the rattling sound, will also recall the visual memory of the rattle snake that the rattling is associated with, and you will take the appropriate precautions to prevent being bitten, even though you don't see the rattle snake.

Predictions

All predictions are the result of learning from experience, and since experience is just memories that result from perceptions, all predictions we make are ultimately the result of information we've taken in through our five senses and recorded as memories. We are not born with any of these memories. As far as the brain is involved, what we are born with is a framework upon which these memories can be built in the neocortex, and we are born with reflexes that we don't have much control over, such as the reflex to breathe as the oxygen tension in the blood decreases. These reflexes are all centered in the more primitive parts of the brain, also known as the brainstem, and are not learned, nor are they the result of experience. The neocortex, incidentally, is the only part of the brain that we are interested in with regards to the information presented in this book, because only the neocortex part of the brain can think, form memories, and define who we are. For instance, if it were possible to switch your brainstem with mine, while leaving both our neocortices intact, no one would be able to tell that there was any difference, just as when someone has a heart or kidney transplant. But if it were possible to exchange only our neocortices, the difference would immediately be obvious and profound, as I would become you, but with my body, and you would become me, but with your body.

Prediction is so pervasive that what we perceive does not come solely from our senses. It is a combination of what we perceive and of our brain's memory-derived predictions. The more we experience the same perception, the more likely we are to expect that perception to continue to be experienced the same way in the future. Let's say I live in a very rural area where there are few cars that travel the road in front of my house. Every morning when I leave for work, I stop at the end of the driveway to look for any cross-traffic before pulling out onto the road. If I had been doing this every day for the past twenty years, and had never seen an oncoming car during that entire time, someday I might go through my usual routine of stopping at the end of the driveway, looking for the non-existent cross-traffic, then pulling out onto the road, only to get broad-sided by an oncoming car. When the police come and ask me why I pulled out in front of the oncoming car, my response will be that I never saw him coming. After so many years of performing the same function without ever seeing a car, my brain eliminated the middle-man, my actual perception of the oncoming car that day, and just automatically sent the message to my conscious brain what it predicted would be perceived – that there would be no oncoming car, rather than what actually occurred. This may seem incredible, but it frequently occurs with all of us. The more often a certain occurrence is perceived, the more likely it will be predicted to occur by the brain in the future, even without "consulting" the actual next perception of that event when it occurs. If baggage inspectors at airports are looking for weapons in passengers' luggage, and haven't found any for several hours, there's a pretty good chance that they'll miss it if one should happen to appear near the end of their shift because, by that time, their brains are paying more attention to predictions than actual perceptions. You perceive what you expect to perceive, and the more times you perceive the same event, the stronger your expectations are to perceive it that way again.

Thoughts and memories are also linked. A thought cannot occur without activating a memory of something first. Once that stored memory is activated, then a prediction can be made about what will follow. This is what a thought is. There is a random electric impulse generator in the brain that can be directed to the various memories during this thought process. Once a memory is activated, then a prediction can be made about some future occurrence involving that memory. Notice that all of this is accomplished without any perceptual information, or at least none that makes its way to the conscious brain. That is, some perceptions are not considered important enough by the brain to be dealt with actively on a conscious level, but they register in the memory system of the brain anyway, and can influence overall decisions in a subconscious way.

We can control the thought process to some degree, but not completely. As everyone knows, we sometimes have thoughts that we don't want, but just can't seem to get out of our mind. In these cases, there is something in the brain that directs the electric impulse generator to the memories associated with the thoughts we are trying to forget about. The emotional centers of the brain are strong driving forces for thought production. Because of this, perceptions that activate the emotional areas of the brain are more likely to trigger thought production. If I'm at work and someone says something rude to me, I might feel angry about it. When I go home that night, I may keep playing the incident over and over in my brain to the point where I can't get to sleep. As hard as I might try to deactivate that memory, it may be very difficult because of its emotional content.

When we daydream, we let our predictions take the place of perceptual information. A memory is activated and brought into consciousness, and then predictions are made, based on that memory. We do this frequently as we plan for the future, worry about upcoming events, or go over past events.

SLEEP

There have been lots of books and articles written about the subject of sleep. We are all interested in sleep because we're all affected by it, it takes up about a third of the time we spend on earth, and if it doesn't occur like it's supposed to, it adversely affects our lives. Sleep has an aura of mystery. It's a period of time when we are extremely vulnerable because we are in an unconscious state.

We occasionally hear that no one knows why we sleep, but this is completely false because the reason we need to sleep has been fairly well described. We have to sleep to allow the permanent storing of information from the previous awake period. We perceive a lot during our awake periods, and a great deal of the information we perceive needs to be stored as permanent memories, which require changes and additions to the framework of the neocortex part of the brain. All of this requires a huge expenditure of energy – remember that although the brain is only two percent of the mass of our bodies, it is responsible for twenty-five percent of our daily energy consumption. There is no way that the formation of permanent memories could ever keep up with the amount of perceived information we take in during the waking hours if we didn't have a break of eight hours or so when no new perceptual information is being received. Not only does sleep allow time to form permanent memories, but it also decreases, by about a third, the amount of time we spend each day perceiving information.

There are five stages of sleep. Stages I through IV are progressively deeper stages of sleep, and REM (rapid eye movement) sleep is comparable to stage I sleep in being a lighter stage of sleep. During REM sleep, very vivid dreams occur. REM sleep is the only stage of sleep in which the brain is electrically blocked from sending electric impulses to the muscles. Some scientists feel that this is a protective measure for us, from an evolutionary standpoint, because we have our most animated dreams during REM sleep, and paralyzing our muscles, in effect, prevents us from injuring ourselves while sleeping as we attempt to act out these animated dreams.

We dream in all five stages of sleep, but we can only recall dreams that occur during stage I, II, and REM sleep because we aren't as deeply unconscious during these stages. How do we know that we dream in stage III and IV of sleep if we can't recall dreams from those stages of sleep? It's because we know that electric impulses are constantly traveling randomly around the brain, even when we're sleeping, and whenever an electric impulse in the brain travels along a wire that codes for a particular memory, that memory will be activated, either consciously if we're awake, or subconsciously if we're asleep. It really couldn't be any other way, or we'd have to say that electric impulses that travel along wires that code for memories sometimes activate those memories and sometimes they don't. That would be like saying that sometimes when you light a fire, heat is produced, while other times no heat is produced when you light the fire.

What is the significance of dreams? Sigmund Freud spent a lifetime studying the hidden meanings of dreams. During his time, there was very little known about how the brain worked, but now that we know a lot more about how the brain functions, we can better explain the significance of dreams. Dreams occur randomly as the impulse generator in the brain sends electrical impulses throughout the brain while we sleep. Whenever a particular memory is recalled by a random impulse that happens to travel down that particular memory wire, then that memory becomes part of a dream. Since the random impulse generator has no specific memory it is trying to activate, it will jump from one to another, which is why we seem to be in a car one minute and on a train the next minute during a dream. People also seem more likely to dream about something that is more current and important in their lives. This is because the memories of these events are being "worked on" to be made more permanent during sleep, and so there will be more electrical impulses directed toward these newly forming memories during sleep to make them permanent, which will be more likely to activate them to become part of that night's dreams. The more important a perception is, the more time will be spent on making sure the memory of it is made more permanent while a person sleeps. If you had a very difficult day at work with your boss, you will probably be thinking about this constantly, and your brain will be furiously making memories relating to what was perceived that day so that you can ultimately make predictions about what will happen or what you will do about your concerns in the future. (Remember from an earlier section that the reason for making memories is for the purpose of making future predictions.) This "memory-making" will continue while you are sleeping, and you will probably spend a great deal of time dreaming about the occurrences of that day as all the memories pertaining to the difficulties you had with your boss are made permanent while you sleep.

How does the brain differentiate a dream from an actual perception? Sometimes we have dreams that seem so real that it takes us awhile after we awaken to realize that they're not based on actual occurrences, or perceptions. There are a few reasons we're able to tell the difference between a dream and a perception. First, the timing of a dream lets us know that it was actually a dream. A very vivid dream usually causes us to awaken either during or right after it, at which point we're quickly aware that it was a dream. Second, because a dream is a sequence of fairly random stimulations of memory wires, it usually doesn't follow a sequence of events that would logically be followed during an awake perception. Third, there is an area in the brain that is active when we are awake and inactive when we are asleep. This area of the brain, called the reticular activating system, is involved when perceptions occur, but not when dreams occur. Since it's associated with the awake state, things that occur when not awake don't register as awake events. Sometimes, however, in people who have had various diseases of the brain, this system can go awry, and vivid dreams can be misinterpreted as real. I once had a patient who had suffered several mini-strokes over the years. These are small dead areas of the brain that result from poor blood flow through the arteries of the brain, and are common with advancing age. This patient's family reported that he would often wake up in the morning with a story to tell about something that happened when he was asleep. In spite of his family's explaining to him that these were just dreams, he would have no part of it. Until the day he finally died, he swore that what were obviously dreams had actually occurred. In his case, there was almost certainly some type of interruption in the pathways in the brain that were related to the reticular activating system that made it difficult for him to tell the difference between what occurred while awake and asleep.

NEUROTRANSMITTERS

So far, I've been discussing the nerves that carry perceptive information to the brain as well as the nerves within the brain that are modified to form memories, and I have been referring to these nerves as "living wires." Something that has not been mentioned yet is how the electric impulse gets from one nerve, or wire, to the next one. If the entire nervous system were made up of one continuous wire, like a giant ball of string, then it wouldn't matter, as every wire would actually be a continuation of the same wire. That's not the way it works in the brain, though. As I mentioned previously, there are several billion separate wires in the brain, each of which has an average of one thousand connections to other wires, resulting in several trillion connections of different wires. How are these connections made? The most logical method would seem to be that when a wire connects to another wire, it should just stick to that wire, kind of like the way the different pieces of a car body are welded together. This is not the way the wires connect to each other, though. In fact, they aren't physically attached to each other at all. There is a very small gap that separates the tip of the impulse-sending wire from the wire that will be receiving the electric impulse. When the electric signal reaches the tip of the sending wire, it triggers the release of chemicals, called neurotransmitters, from the tip. These neurotransmitters then diffuse very quickly across the gap between the two wires. When they come into contact with the receiving wire, they trigger an electric impulse that then continues along the receiving wire.

There is a very good reason why transmission of electric signals between wires should proceed via chemicals rather than by direct contact. By using chemicals, the strength of the impulse that bridges the gap can be modified, and modifying the strength of the impulse allows strengthening the bond between the two wires. The more often an impulse is sent to a particular junction, the more chemical the tip makes to release at that junction, thus making the junction a stronger one – one that will more likely trigger a continuation of the electric impulse in the receiving wire. This is the whole basis of how memory is formed. Memory requires stronger junctions to be formed between the wires that make up that particular memory in order to become permanent and lasting. This amplification of impulse signal by permanently altering the chemical-releasing ability of the tip of the sending wire is exactly what is needed to accomplish this strengthening of the gap junction. There are some other modifications made at the gap junction to make the connection stronger as well, but the purpose is ultimately the same – to strengthen the connection to form a lasting memory that can be recalled more easily. If the wires were connected together like a weld, where they were in direct contact with each other, it would be much more difficult to modify the strength of the connection, and consequently, forming memories would be more difficult to do as well.

There are several different kinds of neurotransmitters used by our brain. Some of them work fast, to trigger a quick reaction in the receiving wire, while others work slow, so that it takes longer for the impulse from the tip of one wire to trigger a continuation of the electric impulse in the receiving wire. The neurotransmitters are also classified by whether they exert a positive or negative effect on the receiving wire. Excitatory neurotransmitters cause increased activity in the receiving wire, while inhibitory neuro-transmitters cause a decreased likelihood that the electric impulse arriving at the tip of the sending wire will continue on across the gap junction and then along the receiving wire. Why would we need different types of neurotransmitters that work fast or slow, or can either increase or decrease the chances of an electric impulse being transmitted across a gap junction to continue along its path? We need the faster neurotransmitters because they allow a quicker response to a stimulus. For instance, if we're out in the forest and see a bear, we don't want to wait very long between the time of the stimulus of seeing him and the response of running away. The faster neurotransmitters allow a quicker reaction time. However, when our brain is trying to permanently modify a gap junction so that a permanent memory can be formed, a neurotransmitter that works more slowly allows the stimulus from the sending wire to "hang around" longer in the gap junction so that the modifications needed to make the memory permanent can be under the influence of the neurotransmitter for a longer period of time, allowing the modifications to proceed as required. In this case, a slower neurotransmitter is required.

Excitatory neurotransmitters make it easier for an impulse to be transmitted from one wire to another, while inhibitory neurotransmitters make it more difficult for that transmission to occur. If there were no way to shut down the effects of the excitatory neurotransmitters, reverberation cycles would result, where an impulse would just keep circling around the brain without stopping, kind of like the feedback a guitar player gets when he stands too close to the sound system – the sound vibration of the speakers causes the guitar strings to vibrate, which then causes more sound being fed back to the speakers, which causes even more vibration of the guitar strings, and so on. Inhibitory neurotransmitters prevent these reverberation cycles, and calm down the electrical activity in the brain. In fact, many anti-seizure medications consist of large doses of inhibitory neurotransmitters to shut down the over-activity of the brain, preventing seizures. (A seizure is an excessive amount of uncontrolled electrical stimulation of the wires of the brain that often spreads to include other areas of the brain as well.)

Although it is not my intention to bog down the reader with the names of the various neurotransmitters, as they're really not important for my purposes in this book, I mention them here, along with some of their associated actions found through research, because you have probably seen them mentioned in various newspaper articles and news reports, and it may put some of what we've been discussing in perspective.

The fast-acting neurotransmitters of the brain include glutamate, which is excitatory, and GABA, which is inhibitory. The slow neurotransmitters include the peptides (opiates, such as endorphins and enkephalins), amines (serotonin, epinephrine, norepinephrine, and dopamine), and the hormones. All our perceptive abilities rely on the two fast neurotransmitters, GABA and glutamate, with slower modulation by the peptides, amines, and hormones.

Dopamine is the neurotransmitter that anticipates rewards it expects the brain to receive, and sends off an alarm if the reward either exceeds or falls below the anticipated level. It is the neurotransmitter of novelty and surprise. It is released in the amount anticipated by a novelty, but if the novelty is not up to expectations, then cravings result. It has been found that people who have higher levels of dopamine than normal are more prone to dependency and craving, the symptoms of addiction. Elevated concentrations of dopamine in the brain produce exhilaration, increased energy, insomnia, decreased appetite, a pounding heart, hyperventilation, and sometimes anxiety and fear. Music can stimulate a release of dopamine in the brain, which can then produce these feelings as well.

The effects of norepinephrine are varied, depending on where in the brain it is used as a neurotransmitter. Most of the effects are similar to dopamine, regarding exhilaration, excessive energy, insomnia, and loss of appetite. It is also associated with increased memory for new stimuli, especially pleasurable perceptions.

Serotonin deals with harm avoidance and confidence. The higher the levels of serotonin in the brain, the more confident one becomes. Low levels of serotonin may be related to aggression, impulsivity, and disinhibition. Low levels of serotonin may also be linked to romantic love.

It should be mentioned that the adage, "moderation in all things" applies to levels of neurotransmitters too. For instance, if someone took a megadose of serotonin, in order to become extremely confident, it wouldn't work, because we are talking about very tiny differences between a lot and a little of a neurotransmitter in the brain. Too much of any neurotransmitter in the brain will have unpredictable, and certainly unfavorable, results.

Acetylcholine is used mainly outside the brain to move muscles, but it can also act as a fast neurotransmitter inside the brain, as well as a slow modulator, depending on where it's working.

Oxytocin is a hormone that is released in response to various bodily needs, such as hunger, thirst, uterine contractions, milk production, and control of body temperature. It also is the "trust" mediator. That is, higher levels of this hormone cause one to become more trusting of others. Oxytocin is also the pair-bonding hormone for females, while vasopressin is the pair-bonding hormone for males. These are triggered for release in the brain by estrogen and testosterone, respectively, in females and males.

PERSONALITY

What is personality? Everybody has a unique one, and when we meet people for the first time, we can usually tell fairly quickly if theirs is a type that is compatible with ours. Personality is not some mystical aura that surrounds a person. It is nothing more than the response of the brain to the summation of all the perceptions a person has experienced and recorded as memories, both consciously and subconsciously. We don't have to be conscious of perceptions to respond to them. For instance, when you feel cold at night while you're asleep, you will pull the blanket up over yourself in response, even though you're sound asleep at that time.

The forming of a person's distinct personality begins even before birth, once the fetal brain has developed to the point where it can receive perceptive information. Fetuses are not pre-programmed to react. They react because of unconscious perceptions in utero. In the fetus, perception is usually only via the sense of touch, and possibly the sense of hearing. As mentioned earlier, reflexes, such as breathing or tensing up at the sound of a loud noise, are the only responses that are pre-programmed. Shy people are not pre-programmed to be shy, nor are outgoing people pre-programmed to be outgoing. The framework in the brain upon which all the memories are to be stored is genetically programmed, but all the memories that are stored on this framework are the result of perceptive information arriving in the brain through one or more of the five senses, and that perceptive information is what determines a person's personality. This includes emotions, morals, ethics, and everything else that makes up an individual's personality. They are all the result of something that was perceived, then stored as a memory somewhere in the brain, ready to be recalled to make a prediction and then a response the next time information is perceived that is either the same or very similar.

The only way we know anything is from direct perception (experience) or from indirect perception (someone teaching information to us). What follows from this is that we can only react to a perception using what we know, or have memories about, through previous perceptions. For instance, if I meet you for the very first time at a company picnic, and you immediately feel a sense of fear or anxiety when we begin talking, even though you've never seen, spoken with, or even heard of me in the past, you might quickly excuse yourself and leave my presence. I would, of course, think that you had a very strange personality. But let's look at what's really going on here. You could not possibly react to me in that way unless you had prior perceptive sensory information that had caused memories to be formed in your brain that caused you to make the prediction that I was a threat to you. This means that sometime in the past, you had a bad experience with someone who either looked like me, had the same mannerisms as me, or sounded enough like me that when you perceived me for the first time, and the sensory information about me traveled to your brain looking for a memory to compare me to so that a prediction and response could be made, the closest memory found was of someone similar to me which had also associated a memory of that person together with a memory for fear and anxiety. This would be a direct perception, or a perception from personal experience. If someone had told you before the picnic to watch out for me because I was a real jerk, and then you met me and reacted in the same fearful or anxious manner, even though you had never met me before, that would be an example of an indirect perception, or the result of someone relaying sensory information to you. Our personalities and behaviors are the responses we exhibit, based on previous sensory stimuli we have been exposed to, and nothing more. The implications of this will be discussed at greater length in Part II.

EMOTIONS

"Sticks and stones may break my bones, but words will never hurt me!" Have you ever heard this statement before? It's meant to show someone who's taunting us that his unkind words have no effect on us. The truth is that the statement couldn't be more wrong. Taunting words can, and do, affect our brain as much as being hit with sticks and stones, but via a different perceptive route. The perception of the pain inflicted from sticks and stones enters the brain by way of the sense of touch. The perception of the taunting words enters the brain by way of the sense of hearing. Once the perception reaches the brain from either of these two senses, it is compared with a previous memory of the same, or very similar, perception. Because these are both very strong perceptions, they will be associated with memories in the emotional areas of the brain and will subsequently cause a strong response. More attention will be directed to dealing with these incoming perceptions than to our usual perceptions because they include memories in the area of the emotional centers in the brain. More predictions will be made. That is, when the memory that matches these perceptions is recalled, the awareness of it will last much longer than usual while a response to the perception is being planned. In other words, the brain will focus much more intently on how to respond to either of these perceptions than it would focus on a response to someone asking us to pass the sugar, for example. The result of all this intense focus will be amazingly similar. Both types of perceptions may trigger a response that includes crying, retaliation, self-doubt, or anxiety. Of course, if the sticks and stones break some bones and sever major arteries, this will certainly cause more problems for the victim's well-being, especially if there is a huge loss of blood and the brain is deprived of nutrients for any length of time. The point here is that any perception that is strong enough to trigger recalling a memory in the emotional area of the brain will be paid much more attention than a perception that does not trigger a memory in the emotional center of the brain. So, whether it's sticks and stones or harsh words, either of these two stimuli can hurt by triggering an emotional response.

Strong perceptions cause memories to be formed in the emotional areas of the brain. In fact, emotions are simply memories of more intense, or stronger, perceptions. Our emotional state is completely formed from, and dependent upon, all the strong perceptions we've made memories of. When these strong perceptions are repeated, they will necessarily elicit a strong response from the brain. When someone says, "Don't be so emotional," this makes about as much sense as saying,

"Don't have blue eyes." Our emotional state is based entirely on what we've perceived during our lifetimes. It can't be controlled at will. When a perception reaches the brain, and it matches a memory of a strong perception that had been recorded previously, there's no way the brain can interpret this perception except as a strong one. Emotional people will always be emotional people, and unemotional people will always be unemotional people. It is neither beneficial nor detrimental to be more emotional or less emotional. It's just part of what makes each of us different from one another. How we perceive determines how we react. (We will deal with emotions in more detail in subsequent chapters.)

CONCENTRATION

When a batter walks up to the plate in the bottom of the ninth with the bases loaded, two outs, and his team losing by two runs, the last thing the coach yells at him before he steps into the batter's box is to concentrate. When the coach says this, what does he mean? What he means is that he wants the batter to pay no attention to all the fans yelling, the opposing players moving around on the field, and the pain that's been bothering him in his right leg since he slid into second base five innings ago. What the coach wants is for the batter to block out all conscious perception except the visual perception of the baseball being thrown by the pitcher. If the player is able to do that, he allows the light reflected off the baseball to reach the back of his eyes, where it triggers an electric impulse that travels along a living wire to the visual area of the brain, looking for a memory that compares equally to the pitched ball, regarding its speed, its arc, and its location. If the brain locates a memory that matches this thrown pitch, a prediction will be made, based on this memory, about whether the pitch will cross the plate in an area where he can hit it. If the prediction is that it will cross the plate in an area where he can hit it, then the brain will send an electric impulse to the muscles of the batter's arms, causing him to swing the bat at the ball. Meanwhile, the ball is traveling a mere sixty feet at over ninety miles per hour, so he has to make his decision about whether to swing or not fairly quickly. If he's also receiving perceptual information about where the opposing players are moving on the field, what a heckler is yelling at him while he's batting, and how much his leg hurts, all these perceptions are competing with the perception of the thrown baseball for attention in the brain. If the brain has to deal with all these perceptions at one time, it will necessarily take a longer time to deal with the perception of the thrown baseball, and by the time the batter reacts to the thrown base-ball, it will already be in the catcher's mitt. If the batter is able to block out all the extraneous perceptive information and only pay attention to the ball being pitched, he can react faster, in-creasing his chances of hitting it.

Increasing our attention to incoming sensory information also alters that information so that it is perceived differently by the brain than if we weren't concentrating so hard. The way this works is that the contrast between the various parts of a perception are amplified with increasing attention. For in-stance, using the example of the pixels on a computer monitor again to represent the receptors for light in the back of the eye, let's say we've got three columns of three pixels in each column (a very small section of the receptive area of the retina). We will then concentrate very hard on a picture of a yellow banana lying on a blue table, and the light reflected into the eye from the picture will stimulate all nine of these receptors (pixels). Each one of the receptors will send a signal to the vision center of the brain. Let's suppose we chose our nine-pixel representation of the picture so that it is right where the yellow banana meets the blue table. In that case, the three pixels in a vertical column to the right of center will each send an impulse to the brain representing yellow for the banana, while the three pixels in a vertical column to the left of the center row will each send an impulse to the brain representing blue for the table. The three pixels in the center will each send a bluish-yellow, or greenish impulse to the brain, representing a transition from the banana to the table. So if we look at all nine pixels at one time, we'll see yellow fading to greenish fading to blue. When we increase our attention to the picture of the yellow banana on the blue table, it allows the electric signals from the yellow row and from the blue row to send additional branches of electric impulses to the area of the brain that receives the transitional greenish-colored impulses, and these branched electric impulses from both the yellow and the blue receiving wires effectively inhibit the greenish electric impulses from being received in the brain. This is usually done by using an inhibitory neurotransmitter to stop the greenish impulse, or by sending an impulse backwards along the receiving green wire to intercept and cancel the incoming greenish perception before it is received by the memory system of the brain. The result is that the vertical blue line of receptors and the vertical yellow line of receptors are received by the brain, but the transitional vertical greenish line is blocked. The brain now visualizes the perception as a well-demarcated sharp line between the blue table and the yellow banana, rather than a fuzzy, gradual change from yellow to green to blue. The picture shows much more contrast. The implications of this are that two different people can perceive the same sensory information differently, depending on each person's frame of reference and how focused he is on it. This will be discussed further in the chapter on relativity.

THE HIPPOCAMPUS

I haven't mentioned the hippocampus yet, and I don't want the reader to be too concerned about the names of different parts of the brain, because almost none of them are important to remember for purposes of this book. But the hippocampus should be mentioned here because it is the part of the brain that all perceptive information must pass through before a permanent memory of that perceptive information can be made in the neocortex of the brain. It can be thought of as a temporary holding area for "memories in the making." You can instantly remember a new perception in the hippocampus for a relatively short period of time, usually a few minutes, but you will permanently remember it in the neocortex only if you experience it over and over, either via more perceptions of it, or by thinking about it (recalling it from the hippocampus over and over). If the incoming perception is not deemed important enough by the brain to remember, meaning that when it was compared to other identical or similar memories, it didn't require a new response than would normally be made to a perception of that type, then the memory of it in the hippocampus will shortly be replaced by other incoming perceptions. But if the new perception is different enough from previous perceptions, as well as being something that the brain determines is important to remember, or is something that elicits a strong response from the brain, then the hippocampus will cause a permanent memory of it to be formed.

Since the hippocampus is capable of holding incoming perceptions as memories for only a few minutes before the electric impulse of that perception dissipates and is replaced by more incoming perceptions, an interesting predicament can result. Suppose you're coming home from work some night and just as you open the door to your house, you turn around and see a man standing there, ready to rob you. You see his face very clearly, and then he hits you over the head with a heavy object and knocks you out. When you regain consciousness several minutes later, you call the police and they ask you what the man looked like. You tell them you don't know and you are absolutely correct because when he knocked you out immediately after you saw him, the memory of his facial features was only represented in the temporary memory of your hippocampus. Once he knocked you out, that information, which was stored as temporary electric signals in the hippocampus, dissipated and was lost from your brain. In fact, everything temporarily stored in your hippocampus from the previous four or five minutes was also lost. That's why people can't remember the details of an auto accident they may have been involved in if they lost consciousness at the time of the accident. This information is lost forever and there is no way that it can ever be recalled, no matter how intensely the victim is interrogated.

The hippocampus is also the electric impulse generator that sends electric signals around the brain trying to locate a memory we are trying to recall. If we are thinking about something, or even just daydreaming, the hippocampus is involved.

SUMMARY

The reason our brain works so well is because it associates both new perceptions and memories of old perceptions together, rather than trying to look at each perception individually as a new and isolated event. There is no specific plan laid out for the brain, other than the very basic framework upon which all the memories of perceptions are built. If there were some kind of plan to the brain, the amount of information needed to encode such a vastly complex scheme would exceed the information capacity of the brain itself, let alone the coding capacity of our DNA. For instance, as mentioned earlier, there are billions of different wires in the brain, each of which makes thousands of connections to other wires. To have a plan ahead of time for how all these wires would be individually formed and connected would be impossible. However, there are some facets of the brain that are coded for in the genetic material. It is more efficient for the brain to automate the processes that get repeated a lot, such as breathing and various reflexes, like coughing when something is lodged in the throat. These processes eventually become encoded in our genes for the simple reason that they are the same in everyone and they shouldn't vary from person to person anyway because they are essential for survival. They are much simpler in complexity and fewer in number too, so they don't take up a large amount of the genetic material for coding.

What about mistakes? Based on everything we've discussed in this chapter, from perceptive information being received at a sensory receptor, then being converted to an electric impulse that travels to the brain where it is compared to memories of previous perceptions, then acted upon, if necessary, it doesn't appear that we should ever make the mistakes we humans are known for. Mistakes are the result of initiating a response to perceptive input without adequate memories. For instance, you might be sitting in a biology class taking notes from the instructor and begin daydreaming for a few moments. During that brief time, the instructor may have mentioned a key point about the subject that you failed to receive as a new perception. When the time comes to use that information, you won't have a memory of it, and will try to solve a problem without using it, resulting in mistakes. Since mistakes can come from problems with attention or from acting without an adequate fund of knowledge to obtain the appropriate response, it would seem more logical to respond only to the depth of information we have in our possession, which is in the form of memories of perceptions. The problem is we don't always know that we don't have an adequate basis on which to make responses. We respond based on what we think is adequate to handle what the situation calls for, and if it turns out that the fund of knowledge is not deep enough, then mistakes will likely result.

When we revisit perception in a later chapter, you will also see that, from a memory-forming standpoint, we learn much more from our mistakes than from our successes. That is, memories of responses that result in failures, or mistakes, become much more permanent in our brain than memories of successes.

LANGUAGE

Language is the one thing that separates us from the rest of the animal kingdom, allowing our superiority to manifest itself, right? One only has to observe a few other species to see that this is not true. Birds communicate with their bird language, and monkeys communicate with their monkey language. They don't understand our language, but then, we don't understand theirs either, for the most part. Sometimes we even have difficulty understanding our own language. For instance, here is an actual excerpt from a recorded property deed:

"Witnesseth, Grantor, for and in consideration of the sum of Ten and No/100ths Dollars in hand paid, and love and affection, the receipt and sufficiency of which are hereby quit-claimed and does by these presents bargain, sell, remise, release, and forever quit-claim to Grantee all the right, title, interest, claim or demand which Grantor has or may have had in and to all that tract or parcel described on Exhibit attached hereto and by this reference made a part hereof."

Does this mean that somebody sold a piece of property to someone else for ten dollars?

The thing that sets us apart from other animals, regarding language, is that our brain is so much more complex that we can do more things with language than other species of animals can do with theirs. It's not a matter of our having something special that no other animal has, it's a matter of having so much more of it that we can do more complicated things with it. As was stated in the previous chapter regarding our five senses, there is also nothing magical about human language either. For instance, we use our language to teach others how to avoid danger, but birds do the same thing. Their language is just much more limited, consisting of a specific call or whistle to warn of impending danger, while ours may consist of a lengthy statement to warn someone.

Language does not always convey to the listener what the speaker means. For example, I've read that "language has its origins in our genetic material." Does this mean that part of the basic framework upon which all our memories are eventually stored is specifically designed and coded for by our DNA to only store language-related memories, or does it mean that our DNA has an actual code for each individual word that we use, or does it mean something else? As you can see, even the language we use to describe language and its origins can be ambiguous. (Hopefully, whoever wrote the statement that language has its origins in our genetic material meant that our DNA codes for a generalized framework upon which language memories can be built, along with all our other memories, because any other meaning intended by the author of the statement would be wrong.)

RELATIONSHIP TO MEMORY

One of the most unique things about language is that it allows us to form permanent memories of events without having actually perceived those events with our own senses. This feat occurs many times a day when parents tell their children not to cross the street without looking both ways or they might be hit by a car. By hearing this over and over every day, a child's brain will form a permanent memory of this auditory warning. One day, the ball the child is playing with may roll into the street. He starts running after it, but as he reaches the street, the perception of his running into the street travels into his brain looking for a memory to compare this new perception to in order to determine if any kind of a response is indicated by any memories that compare with this new perception. The memory of his parents' spoken warning about looking both ways before running into the streets to avoid being hit by a car is activated, and the response dictated by this memory is to look both ways before he steps out onto the street. He will then look both ways, since that is what the memory dictates should be the appropriate response to that particular perception. He has formed a permanent memory of what to do in the event the need arises to cross a street, even though he had never perceived, or experienced, that event before. Memories gained in this more passive way through language are usually not as permanently formed in the brain as memories of active perceptions. For instance, the child in the previous example is much more likely to remember not to run out into the street without looking for oncoming cars first if he does happen to run out into the street, then hears a loud squealing of tires, looks up, and sees a car screeching to a stop, just barely missing him. In this case, a much more permanent memory will be formed of the perception because it will also be stored in the emotional area of the brain where memories of fear are usually found. The result is that the next time his ball goes into the street, he will be more likely to look for cars first before stepping into the street.

Through language, not only can we gain memories of perceptions without actively perceiving them, but we can also think about these passive perceptions and make even more memories through our thought processes. In this way, we can come up with completely new ideas without ever having actively perceived anything that was related to the final idea. This is the real power of language. For instance, you may be reading an article in the newspaper that says a robber was caught when the police got some fingerprints off a glass by using masking tape to lift them from the glass. You never knew they used masking tape to lift fingerprints off glasses, but you think about this and come to the conclusion that cellophane tape would work a lot better. Even though you've never actively perceived a fingerprint being lifted from an article before, you have come up with a way that this process can be done much more efficiently.

Language is essential for the thought process that takes place within the brain. When we perceive something, then compare it to memories already in the brain, then make predictions about future events based on these comparisons, all of this information that gets shuffled around the association areas of the brain during this thought process requires language as a medium. Without language, there is no thought process. For instance, on a Tuesday you look at a clock and perceive that it's 3:30 PM. This perception travels from your eyes to the visual memory area of the brain, where it's compared to memories of what usually occurs at this time on Tuesdays, and the response associated with this perception is to get in your car to go pick up the kids at school. You then process this information along even further by associating it with other memory areas of the brain and add another response to this perception, this being that you also have to pick up some food at the grocery store for supper tonight, and you have to meet a client at 4:30 PM after that. All of this planning in the association areas of the brain takes place using language. In fact, the language can be so pervasive that part of the response to all of these thoughts might be to send electric impulses to move the muscles of the vocal cords, and you will actually say out loud to yourself what you're thinking.

Let's say that instead of using language to map out all the plans mentioned above, you use colors instead, since we can store perceptions of colors as memories without first converting the colors to language. So, at 3:30 PM on Tuesday when you look at the clock, that perception compares to the memory in your brain for the color blue. This reminds you that after that, you have to do yellow, and then at 4:30 PM, the color red comes into play. It doesn't make much sense, does it? The only way we can think, plan, or predict anything is by using language as a medium.

Language does not have to consist of spoken words, initiated in the usual way by passing air through the vocal cords, it just has to consist of some method of conveying a thought from one person to another, or from one part of the brain to another part of the brain. For instance, there is a tribe of bushmen that use shrill whistles as their language because they live far enough apart in mountainous regions that their speaking voice won't carry as well as whistling does. The length of each whistle and the intonation associated with it take the place of words. If one person gives a series of five different length whistles and intonations to a friend on a neighboring hill, this may mean, "Come to my house tonight." In this case, memories would be stored as a series of different length whistles and intonations, all of which could easily be joined together and added to in the whistlers' brains to achieve comparisons of perceptions to memories, make predictions based on those memories, and to effect a response based on all this information. When one of these bushmen sits in front of his hut daydreaming, he replays whistles in his mind, not words like we are familiar with, formed by altering the shape of the vocal cords.

An obvious problem with language is that it would be almost useless if it were only understood by the person using it. Let's look at two scenarios.

First, suppose that you are the only person on earth. Everyone else was wiped out by a vicious virus within a day or so after you were born and you were the only survivor, left to be suckled by wolves until you were old enough to find food on your own. You have never been exposed to language. Would you be able to think? In other words, as you perceived things through your five senses over the course of your lifetime, and made memories of those perceptions, then you compared other perceptions to those memories to initiate appropriate responses to the new perceptions, would you be able to come up with new predictions based on thought processes that utilize the memories of perceptions you have stored in your brain? If language is genetically coded in our DNA, then you might be able to think, using the genetically coded information about language, but you would have to develop your own "dictionary" of words, since you would never have been exposed to any. However, if language development is a product of the environment, as we're fairly sure it is, meaning that it won't develop unless you learn it from someone else via perception of language use by others, then you probably would not be able to think and make predictions based on thought processes. This would mean that all you would be able to do is perceive something new, make a permanent memory of it if it's something you perceive on a regular basis, and by trial and error, respond to the perception in a manner that has been determined by this trial and error method to give the best results for your survival. You would, in effect, be reduced to a stimulus – response machine with no ability for thought. If an animal bit you during your daily search for food, your brain would form a memory of that perception. The next time you came across an animal like that, you would respond by avoiding it. There would be no further thought process involved. For instance, you wouldn't be able to plan ahead to take a weapon with you the next time you traveled in areas where those types of animals roam.

Since no one has ever performed a study where a person was kept from being exposed to language to see what happens, we don't know with certainty whether language is specifically coded for in the genetic material, or if it is an environmental phenomenon. However, we think that the genetic material does not code for language simply because, from a logistics standpoint, it would appear to require much more genetic material to code for language than we have available. So it's almost certain that if one is never exposed to language, that person will never be able to think. In fact, that person would be no better off, intellectually, than any other animal in the forest.

The second problem with language is that the words used by one person may not be understood by another person. In this case, no passive perception by verbal communication can cause any permanent memories to be formed because the brain won't recognize the message in the unknown language as being something worth remembering. In order to form permanent memories of perceptions that have never been actively perceived, a person has to have previous memories of what the words used in communicating the passive perceptions to him mean. For instance, if someone told me in Russian that his job was ringing the church bells, so I'd better hold my hands over my ears because he had set the church bells to ring in one minute, I would hear his words as a new perception, then try to find a memory to compare them to that would let me then make an appropriate response, but I would find no matching memories for the message nor the words used to form the message because I don't understand Russian. And since his words sound like gibberish to me, rather than language, my brain would have no reason to form a memory of them. One minute later, the church bells would ring, my ears would hurt, and I would not be prepared to cover my ears the next time he told me they would ring in one minute, all because my brain had no way of understanding that a memory of what the Russian man had told me should be made.

An interesting aside to the example above is that if I saw this Russian man several times a week, and every few times I saw him he said the same words, which were then followed by the bells ringing one minute later, eventually I would form a memory for those words, based on their frequently repeated sounds and the length of the statement. Even though I didn't know what he was saying literally, I would associate his statement with the bells ringing one minute later and would eventually cover my ears in response to hearing his statement. This is because a memory would now have been formed in my brain for that statement. Then, when I perceived the sound of his voice saying it again, and compared that perception to the memory of the same perception, the appropriate response dictated by recalling the memory would be to cover my ears. This is also how children learn to use words and sentences in their parents' language.

MEANINGS OF WORDS

What is life? At what point does a mass of inert chemicals suddenly become a living thing? Don't these questions sound really thought provoking and philosophical? You can find all kinds of opinions about the answers to these questions in scientific books, philosophical books, social science books, religious books, and even poetry books, but the answer is not as profound as we might like to believe it is. Life is exactly what we say it is, and a mass of inert chemicals suddenly becomes a living thing exactly when we say it does. This is because the limiting factor in defining these concepts is the meanings we have attached to the words we use in our language, not the actual, perceivable change from non-life to life. There may truly be a specific moment that a mass of inert chemicals suddenly becomes a living thing, but we can only describe that moment using language, and language is fraught with inconsistencies that won't allow descriptions of such things as when life begins, as we shall see.

If you read a scientific text, you might find that life is de-fined as the ability to grow and reproduce. As soon as everyone in the scientific community agrees that this is truly what life is, there will be someone, possibly a philosopher, who will come up with an exception. For instance, what about a mountain range made from volcanoes? Whenever the volcano erupts, the mountains grow and reproduce themselves, yet they're clearly not alive. Now the scientists go back to the drawing board and come up with a new explanation of what life is. They add that for life to exist, reproduction has to be by cell division and must involve DNA, the genetic material. Again someone objects and proposes that some viruses divide using RNA instead of DNA, so are they not alive? And, as has been shown throughout his-tory, the debate about what life is or when it begins will go on forever without obtaining a definitive answer because no two people will have the exact same memories associated with the meanings of words from which a particular concept was formed in their brain. For instance, a biologist will have a much differ-ent concept of what constitutes life, based on the memories of the language perceptions he experienced in his scientific train-ing, than a religious cleric would have, based on the memories of the language perceptions he experienced in his theological training.

We can't universally define what life is or when it begins because we're limited by the memories of the language we are equipped with for making additional memories of these con-cepts in our brains. The language is ambiguous because there are no universally specific words we can use that are perfectly clear in explaining to all individuals what life is. Any words we might use to explain it have meanings that can be interpreted differently by different people, based on their individual perceptions and memories of life, and each of these variations of interpretations is equally valid. This creates ambiguity. If I said that life is "eopelswody", and everyone understood that "eopelswody" was an unambiguous meaning of what life is, then there would be no problem. It would be very clear to everyone what life is because everyone would interpret "eopelswody" as the explanation of life in the same way.

It may be easier to understand this if you think in terms of having a sixth sense to perceive the language used to explain our example of the meaning of life. With the present language that we have, we are limited by the words we have and the often ambiguous, or circuitous, definitions we have assigned to these words. For instance, if you look up the word "color" in a dictionary, it might say that it is a "tone." Next you look up "tone," and it might be defined as "hue." Then you look up "hue," and it might be defined as "color." What you've found is a lot of words that can be substituted for others, but none of them explains what "color" is. You have found several meanings of the word "color," but you are no more aware of the essence of "color" now than you were before you looked it up. You have only succeeded in possibly forming some memories of words in your brain that can be used as synonyms for "color," so that if someone mentions the word "hue," you'll be aware that the person is referring to the "color" of something. Add to this that any interpretation of the passive perception you might get from looking up a word in the dictionary may be different than the one I might receive from looking up the same word, and you can see that problems are going to arise when you and I compare what we think the word "color" means. But suppose you and I each had a sixth sense that allowed us to interpret the word "color" in a completely new way. Then we might both understand exactly what the word means on an entirely new level.

Unfortunately, even my explanation requires an interpretation of the meaning of my words by the reader as well, so there are built in limitations to its clarity. However, the point of all this is to show that our explanations of anything rely on the definitions, or meanings, we've each given to words, and the definitions of those words rely on the definitions of more words. Words are great for use as a medium to allow the thought process to take place within each individual's brain, using his own interpretation of the definitions for the words in his own thought processes, but the words are severely limited once they're used to explain a concept to others who have their own memories of the meanings of the words that are not necessarily the same. That is, the concept in question cannot be universally defined in the same way by everyone because everyone has a unique set of perceptions associated with each memory they form in their brain. For instance, if someone told you and I that he just saw a dog, your memory system might picture "dog" as a collie, because that's the type of dog you had when you were young, and is the easiest memory for your brain to activate for comparison when hearing the word "dog." But my memory system might picture a terrier, for the same reasons. Whose version of the memory of "dog" is correct, yours or mine? The phenomenon of naming everything so that we have the medium of language to enable forming memories of it all has a built in confusion factor, due to the lack of an identical interpretation of language by everyone, which is further due to the different circumstances surrounding each individual's perception of the same object or occurrence and the way that perception is formed as a memory in the brain. As long as language is the medium we must use to learn, think, and communicate with others, this problem will never allow a universal answer for concepts such as when life begins.

LANGUAGE USE

Language has three primary uses. It allows forming memories of perceptions that have never been experienced, it enables using memories of perceptions in the thought process, and it enables the communication of thoughts and ideas with others. In the previous sections, we have discussed the first two ways language is utilized. In this section, we will discuss language as a communication tool.

We can attempt to explain something to someone in a variety of different ways besides using normal speech. We can yell, wave our arms, change our facial expressions, or act out a message in mime. In the end, the only thing that matters is what that person's brain perceives as the message we're trying to convey, and if that perception is different from ours, then the language has failed. For instance, if I tell you that I'll meet you at 4 PM to discuss an important issue, and you thought I said we'd meet at 2 PM, chances are that we won't meet, and the language has failed.

The tense of language can also affect the response of the person we are conveying information to. For instance, if I had a diary with an entry in it that was very personal, and you told me that you *had* read my diary, when I perceived those words, the memory that might be activated for comparison would have a component of embarrassment from the emotional memory area of my brain, and my response might be to look down while my face turns red. If, on the other hand, you said that you *will* read my diary, my perception of those words might activate a memory for comparison that contains a component of fear in the emotional memory area of my brain. This would then elicit a response that would cause me to hurry to where the diary was located and hide it before you could see it. Changing the tense of this communication by substituting one word for another caused two completely different responses to the perceived statement.

The manner in which a communication is delivered to another person can cause the communication to be perceived and compared to previous memories differently. If we were sitting on a park bench chatting one day, and I said that I didn't like the cap you were wearing, but I was laughing while I said it, you would perceive this as playful banter, and when the perception of that statement was compared to memories of similar perceptions, there would probably be either no response indicated, or one that had you laughingly mocking my cap in return. However, if I made the same statement to you, but with a very serious facial expression when I said it, you might compare this perception to a memory in your brain that also included a component in the emotional memory area for anger, and your response might be to prepare for a fight with me. The manner in which the same communication was delivered elicited two completely different responses.

Language can be formulated in such a way that it can cause misguided perceptions. In order to influence the jury's perceptions of a man on trial for embezzling company funds, the prosecutor might say to the man, "By the way, do you still beat your wife?" Although this has nothing to do with why the defendant is there, and assumes facts that haven't been proven, the jurors perceive this question as a statement that the defendant has beat his wife in the past. When the perception reaches the brain of each juror and a memory is made of it, the memory will associate the perception of the defendant with the perception of a wife beater, because perceptions that are received together get stored together, as stated in the previous chapter. This association of "defendant" with "wife beater" will have been made in each juror's brain so that whenever each of them activates the memory of the defendant, he will also activate the memory of a wife beater. All of this resulted from a communication by the prosecutor that had no basis in fact, but, nevertheless, caused permanent memories to be formed in the jurors' brains that will likely influence their later decisions regarding the defendant when they decide on the verdict.

These are some of the ways language is used for communication. There are certainly other ways language can be used and manipulated for communication, and all of them require at least two people – a speaker and a listener. They also depend on the listener's ability to form a memory of a perception in a passive way without actually experiencing it with his five senses.

LOGIC AND REASONING

How does the brain perform logic and reasoning? We can be fairly sure that it's going to involve language, perceptions, memories, and thought processes by now. Both logic and reasoning are related to making responses after perceptions are received in the brain.

Logic involves comparing as many memories as possible of previous perceptions to the perception just received in order to arrive at the correct response to that perception. The key point here is that lots of memories are activated for comparison, even those that are only remotely related to the new perception. If there were only one memory in the brain to compare to the incoming perception for effecting a response to the new perception, the response wouldn't be the "logical" choice, it would be the "only" choice. The more memories of different perceptions there are for comparison, the more logical the response can be. For instance, let's say you're the manager of a baseball team and the present situation on the field dictates that you put in a pinch-hitter who can bunt the ball in order to advance the runners. Joe is the only pinch-hitter you've got on the bench, so you put him in to try to bunt. Is Joe the logical choice for a pinch-hitter? No, he's not the "logical" choice, he's the "only" choice. Now let's assume the same situation, but with three pinch-hitters, Joe, Pete, and Yogi, sitting on the bench. The statistics show that Joe is successful in laying down a bunt 30 percent of the time, Pete is successful 50 percent of the time, and Yogi is successful 90 percent of the time. You have enough perceptive information about what the logical response should be, and you put Yogi in to pinch-hit. He is the logical choice. In order to use logic, a choice must be available.

Logic is usually divided into two types – natural logic and symbolic logic. Natural logic involves deductive and inductive thought processing. In very simple terms, deductive thinking involves deriving a specific conclusion from a general statement, while inductive thinking involves deriving a general conclusion from a specific statement. For instance, if I said that all trees have roots, therefore my elm tree has roots, that would be using deductive logic. If I said that my elm tree has roots, therefore all trees have roots, that would be using inductive logic. Symbolic logic involves translating a natural language, such as English, into mathematical symbols, then solving the math equations to determine the most logical conclusion.

Is the logical choice universal? In other words, is the logical response the same for everyone? If it were, that would mean everyone would have to have identical memories in their brain to make the logical response to the same perception universal. Since we already know that nobody has the same memories as anyone else, then we can assume that the logical response pertains only to the individual who is making that response. For instance, using the same example of the pinch-hitters, you, as the manager, know that Joe has a 30 percent chance of laying down a successful bunt, Pete has a 50 percent chance, and Yogi has a 90 percent chance, so the logical choice for you is to pick Yogi to pinch-hit. Now let's suppose that a statistician who likes to keep tabs on all his favorite players happens to know that Yogi's chances of successfully laying down a bunt are really 9 percent, not 90 percent, because you erred by a factor of ten in figuring out Yogi's probability of laying down a successful bunt. If it were up to the statistician to choose a pinch-hitter, the logical choice for him would be Pete, who, at a 50 percent chance of being successful, has the highest probability of laying down a successful bunt. Even though you and the statistician differ in who should be chosen to pinch-hit, both of you have made the logical choice, based on the memories you each had stored in your brain. The logical response to a perception applies only to the person responding to that perception.

Reasoning is similar to logic, but reasoning is more pragmatic. That is, it takes more into consideration before reaching the logical response. While logic can be utilized using nothing more than mathematical symbols in place of words to obtain the best response, reasoning takes into account such things as emotions before arriving at the logical response. Using our same example of the pinch-hitters, with Joe being successful with bunting 30 percent of the time, Pete being successful 50 percent of the time, and Yogi being successful 90 percent of the time, we add to these facts that Yogi's wife just told him this morning that she wants a divorce. You've been watching Yogi during the game and have noticed that he seems very depressed. His shoulders sag, he's not his usual happy self, and he's not very animated as he sits on the bench. You decide that Pete should be your choice for pinch-hitting, even though your statistics say that Yogi has a 40 percent better chance of laying down a successful bunt. You have reasoned that because Yogi is in a depressed mood, his chances of being successful at bunting tonight are less than 50 percent.

Logic does not involve the emotional memory area of the brain, but reasoning does activate memories in the emotional area when deciding on a final response to a perception. We are probably all aware of situations that cause us to think someone's action defies logic, but logic is not the only means of arriving at an appropriate response to a perception. When reasoning is added into the mix, the response to a perception can be drastically different, even though it is still the most appropriate response. For instance, a friend of yours may be dating a man who is an alcoholic, uses illegal drugs, won't work at a steady job, and treats her badly. Your logical response to all these perceptions is that the man should be dumped. Your friend who is dating him also perceives the same things about him, but also reasons that she is very much in love with him, so this memory of intense love in the emotional area of her brain has to be factored in when making the most appropriate response for herself. In her case, the emotional memory of being in love with the man trumps all the memories of the bad perceptions about him, and her reasoned, logical response is to keep dating him.

A very important concept to remember about logic and reasoning is that everyone always chooses the most appropriate response to any perception, based on comparison of that perception to his own memories. It can't be any other way. Our brain is set up to receive perceptual information, compare it to memories of similar perceptions, and then make the most appropriate response dictated by our predictions. Once the perception is received in the brain, the comparison of it to previous similar perceptions proceeds automatically, and the final response is exactly what these comparisons predict will provide the best outcome for us. To put it another way, we always act in our own best interest. We have no other choice. The implications of this are quite thought provoking. They will be discussed in more depth when we revisit perception again in Part II.

We've been discussing how two different people can perceive the same statement from a third person, for example, and respond in equally appropriate, but different, ways to that perceived statement. Now let's look at the reverse situation – how one person can respond very differently to the same statement made by two different people. In order to see how important comparing our past memories of perceptions is to reaching the most logical response to the same new language perception from two different people, let's say you're a philosophy professor now, and you have just given a final exam to your students with the following single question – "Why Life?" Most of the students will write a three-hour essay to properly answer this question in detail. However, you have two students who answer the question with a simple, "Why not?" One of them is an "A" student who has done exceptionally well in your class, answering questions in class with well thought-out answers that show a good understanding of the subject. The other student shows up to class only occasionally, gets "C"s and "D"s on most of his tests, does not participate much in discussions, and when asked a question in class, gives a concrete answer that shows little, if any, insight. You give the "A" student an "A" on the final exam, and you give the other student an "F" for the same answer on the same final exam. Is this logical? In both cases, you compare the perception of the answer to everything you have stored in your memories about each student to arrive at the logical response for each. Even though the language perception you received from each student is identical, the response to each is completely different. Not only can the same perception produce different responses from two different perceivers, but the same perception from two different people can produce different responses by the same perceiver.

SUMMARY

Language is what allows the formation of nearly all our memories, yet it is far from being a precise means of conveying information, as we've seen. Perceived statements may be unclear, prompting false memories to be made; language can be used to deliberately manipulate the memories of the person receiving it; what seems to be a logical response to a perception for one person may seem to be a completely illogical response for another person, even though they both use a logical method of arriving at their different responses; and language often has different meanings for different people, depending on their cache of memories. In the next chapter, we'll look at how mathematics is perceived and dealt with by the brain.

WHO ARE WE, REALLY?

MATH

MATH AS LANGUAGE

What does math have to do with how our brain works or why we think and act the way we do? Math is a language, just like any other language, but with a few modifications. Instead of the twenty-six symbols used in our spoken language that can be strung together to make words and sentences, math uses ten basic symbols that can be strung together to make predictions about quantities. The fact that math is a language means that it can be used to form memories of perceptions that we have not actively experienced with our own five senses, just as with spoken language. For instance, you might tell a child that if you had five apples and gave him three of them, you would have two left. He can then form a permanent math memory of this in his brain without ever seeing the five apples. Math can also be used in our thought processes to make predictions based on stored math memories, just as spoken language does.

The unique thing about math that sets it apart from every other language is that it uses only logic for making predictions about what an appropriate response to an incoming perception should be. There are no math memories located in the emotional memory areas of the brain. While I'm driving along in my car, if I come to a toll bridge that says to deposit one dollar for passage, my response, based on comparing this perception to memories of previous perceptions dealing with math, will be to put some combination of coins totaling one dollar into the till so that the gate will lift, letting me cross the bridge. In searching my memory areas for the proper combination of coins to use, there were no memories from the emotional areas of my brain that were compared to the perception in order to arrive at the correct response. I may feel emotionally angry that the toll is one dollar now when it was only fifty cents last week, causing me to fling the money into the till with a little more momentum, but that has nothing to do with the sequence of events going on in the memory areas of my brain for determining the correct mathematical response required to get the gate to lift and let me pass over the bridge. The math involved in the correct response is all logic with no emotional memory comparison required to arrive at the appropriate response.

The stereotype of someone who is exceptionally gifted at math usually portrays that person as introverted, quiet, and unemotional. This is not just a coincidence. Someone who is exceptionally gifted at solving math problems must have the framework in his brain where all his memories are formed laid out in such a way that there is the least likelihood of interference from the emotional memory areas while he is trying to solve math problems. This allows his thought process to proceed in a logical manner without much interference. On the contrary, people who are exceptionally gifted in emotional endeavors, such as acting, writing poetry, or any such fine arts must have the framework in their brain for storing memories arranged in such a way that the emotional areas of the brain are much more involved in forming responses to incoming sensory information. Brains can be wired favoring one extreme or the other, but are usually more balanced with an approach that doesn't favor either, in terms of using logic or emotion. It would be extremely rare, if not impossible, to find someone who is exceptionally gifted in both the arts and in math, because this would mean that the framework upon which all the memories in his brain are formed would favor both the non-emotional and emotional memory areas at the same time.

Some autistics, schizophrenics, savants, and people with psychological disorders also have an exceptional gift for some talent. That talent almost always requires no emotional memory input when they perceive things that can then be compared to similar memories of other perceptions in their brain. Because of this absence of an emotional component from their stored memories, they are able to arrive at their exceptionally gifted responses. This is for two reasons. First, they are usually labeled as being autistic, schizophrenic, savant, or psychologically abnormal because they are unable to respond appropriately in an emotional way, not necessarily because they are unable to respond in a logical way. Second, their talent, which is almost always one that relies on using logic rather than emotion, is able to manifest itself because there is little or no interference from the emotional memory areas of the brain as they receive a perception, compare it to their stored memories of similar perceptions, then make the appropriate response. This predilection for logical over emotional memory activation still applies to savants who are exceptionally gifted in one of the fine arts, even though one usually associates more memories from the emotional areas being involved with responses to perceptions in someone with exceptional talent in fine arts. For instance, a savant artist is usually very good at reproducing pictures of perceptions in very intricate detail, similar to a copy machine, because he does not use memories from the emotional areas of his brain to give the artwork some feeling. He receives a visual perception and paints exactly what he sees because the memory of that perception is coded exactly as it arrived in the brain, without being modified by input from the emotional memory areas of the brain.

Math language can be mixed with spoken language to produce first responses to perceptions that are incorrect. Our permanent memories for math logic and our permanent memories for spoken logic are stored and recalled separately, so distortions of perceptions can result when spoken language is intermixed with math language. For instance, there is a spoken math problem where farmer A says to farmer B, "If you sell me one of your sheep, I'll have twice as many as you've got." Farmer B responds, "No, you sell me one of your sheep and we'll both have the same amount." At first, when we perceive these statements, our language memories for logic will quickly compare them to memories of logical language and will want to respond that there's no way to exchange just one sheep and have such a drastically different result, depending on whether farmer A gives a sheep to farmer B, or farmer B gives a sheep to farmer A. But upon further analysis using math logic, which takes longer, it can be computed that farmer A has seven sheep and farmer B has five sheep. If this math problem were originally written in algebraic math terms of two equations with two unknowns, so that spoken language was kept out of the problem, the spoken language memories for logic in our brain would not have been activated, and the problem of quickly jumping to the wrong conclusion that it was an impossible situation would have been avoided. Instead, when looking at the problem in algebraic terms, only the math memories in the brain would have been activated and the problem would have been solved mathematically from the beginning without ever considering that it might be an impossible situation.

MATH AND REALITY

Over the past few decades, math has gradually become less and less involved with providing answers for how nature functions, and more and more involved with providing abstract theories and exercises that have little or nothing to do with how nature functions. For instance, with the advent of affordable computers, a lot of math time is being spent on computing various constants with more precision. The value of pi, which we all learned in high school is equal to 3.1416, has now been computed to billions of numbers after the decimal point, at a computer time of several days to months of continuous operation.

Mathematicians delve into the unknown with formulas, not philosophical thought, which sometimes gives unrealistic, though mathematically correct, answers. There is a current theory of matter and energy that requires about ten dimensions, instead of our usual three, in order to work mathematically. When mathematicians are asked if the extra dimensions really exist, they reply that it doesn't matter, and that all that matters is whether mathematical models with extra dimensions provide possible descriptions of the universe. They say that since it cannot be determined mathematically what is real, it is mean-ingless to ask. Shortly, we will provide an answer for this seeming dilemma.

Although math is used to provide an explanation of every-thing that takes place in nature, that doesn't mean that every step along the way to solving math problems has a perceivable consequence in nature. For instance, we can't perceive an in-finity, but mathematicians occasionally divide one infinity into another infinity to get a result that can be a rational number that we can perceive. Math also uses non-perceivable imaginary numbers, like the square root of negative one, in equations that eventually give correct, perceivable, real numbers as answers. You may wonder how the mathematicians can conceive of things like infinities in the first place. Since they can't be per-ceived, how can a person ever form a memory of an infinity? The answer is that we can easily form memories of things we "conceive", even though they can't be "perceived." For in-stance, I can conceive of a horse that has a head on both ends of his body, and can even picture this animal in my mind, even though there is no way an animal like this could ever exist. Concepts do rely on perceptions to "get started," but once a memory of a perception is stored, that perception can be added to by the thought process to conceive of just about anything, possibly even infinities and imaginary numbers. Remember, a *conception* is a memory formed entirely by the thought process in the brain, while a *perception* is anything we experience through our five senses.

Just because something computes mathematically does not make it necessarily perceivable or real. For instance, if you place two flat mirrors so that they face each other, then place an object between them, the math predicts that the object will be reflected back and forth between each of the two mirrors to infinity, with each further reflection slightly smaller than the closer one. This is not consistent with nature, though, because as each reflection becomes smaller, there eventually comes a time when the reflection is so small that it is smaller than the size of one atom, and one atom cannot reproduce a reflection of an entire object. Therefore, the object is not reflected to infinity, but stops at some finite number of reflections.

BEYOND PERCEPTION

We've mentioned that math problems can be solved using infinities and imaginary numbers with very little difficulty, just as easily as if we could actually perceive them. If something can only be explained using math formulas and equations, but can't be applied to something that can be perceived, then it doesn't exist for us. This is important because it means that math can follow all its rules and arrive at mathematically correct answers that we can't perceive, which means that math occasionally functions on a level requiring more sensory information to be perceived than we possess with our mere five senses. The implication of all this is that for us to understand every aspect of math, a sixth sense might be required, such as one that allows perceiving infinities or imaginary numbers, for example.

When Einstein first proposed his ideas on relativity, the mathematics he used to describe them were fairly straightforward and gave answers that were mathematically appropriate and consistent with the ideas he proposed. However, when he tried to explain his ideas using spoken language, they sounded very strange, even preposterous, because spoken language has to refer to something that can be perceived by one or more of our five senses in order for that something to exist for us. To this day, no one has been able to perceive or adequately explain in spoken language some of Einstein's calculations of relativity, even though they have been proven mathematically and by experimentation.

Math does not seem to be as involved with past, present, and future tense as our brain, with its five senses, seems to be. If I had five apples and asked you how many apples I'd have left if I gave you three of them yesterday, or if I gave you three of them tomorrow, your response would be the same – that I would be left with two apples, whether I gave the three apples to you yesterday or will give them to you tomorrow. The math is going to be the same no matter when I give you the three apples. With spoken language, tense can make a big difference in the appropriate response to a perception. My response regarding your reading of my diary in the example in the previous chapter was completely different when you said you *have* read my diary, as opposed to your saying that you *will* read my diary. Perhaps there is a clue in all this that if we had a sixth sense, past, present, and future might not be so important.

SUMMARY

Math uses symbols that form non-emotional, logical, math memories in our brain as we perceive math statements. Math can also utilize intermediate steps that we can't perceive as it works towards a final answer to a problem. This implies that math may require a sixth sense in order for us to perceive everything about it. When we discuss quantum theory in the next chapter on physics, this requirement for a sixth sense will become even more obvious.

WHO ARE WE, REALLY?

PHYSICS AND THE BRAIN

In order to better understand how the brain functions, why some occurrences seem so mysterious or difficult to comprehend, and where everything we perceive came from in the first place, it is now going to be necessary to get into the subject of physics. This chapter will not be a discourse on classical physics like you may have taken in high school or college, as that type of physics is more suited for mathematicians and engineers. This discussion will focus more on theoretical physics and the physics of submicroscopic entities.

Since the brain uses so much energy, it would be nice to know a little bit more about energy. The purpose of this chapter is to explain the mysteries associated with what energy is, where it comes from, and where it will eventually go. Our investigation into the realm of physics will focus mainly on what happens at the very heart of the matter, the tiny interior of the atom. We will delve into such things as quantum theory, gravity, and the "big bang" to get to the answers we need – but don't worry, because there will be no math used or required for understanding these things.

MATTER AND ENERGY

There are all kinds of physics formulas that have energy as one of the terms, yet we don't really know what energy is. The models that are used to describe reactions involving a transfer of energy from one place or one form to another are the creations of researchers' thought processes, ultimately derived from their perceptions. We can perform experiments and look at the results, but all we know for sure is what we started with and what we ended up with. As far as what happened in between, on a submicroscopic level, we must use our imagination to some degree.

It is known that energy involves movement, because there is no energy unless something is moving. We cannot perceive anything unless there is some movement involved, so what we are really perceiving is energy in some form. In order for us to perceive something, some of the energy in what is being perceived has to be transferred to the receptors of one or more of our five senses in such a way that it allows triggering an electric current to travel from the "energized" receptor to our brain so that we can be aware of it. The fact that some energy was transferred from the object perceived to our sensory receptors sometimes means that the total energy that the perceived object contained is now less. For instance, if you sit in front of a fireplace where a log is burning, your touch receptors for temperature are triggered by the heat energy that the log gives off in the form of heat, and as the log loses heat energy, it gets smaller. On the other hand, perception doesn't always include a transfer of energy from whatever is perceived. When you look at an object, the energy that triggers the receptors in your eyes is usually derived from the energy in the light waves reflected off the object you are perceiving, and not energy that actually came out of that object itself.

According to Einstein's most famous formula equating energy to mass, energy and matter can be converted back and forth from one form to the other. From what has been learned about the inner workings of the atom, it appears that when one reaches the smallest single thing that can't be divided any further in an atom, it turns out that it is nothing more than an extremely tiny force field, or energy field. If this force field is to remain in existence, it must move, either by vibrating, circling in a wave-type motion, or by some other type motion. If we could somehow get into the nucleus of the atom to perceive this force field, it would be invisible to the eye, but would still be perceivable through one of our specialized touch receptors. We'd feel an attraction towards it, or a repulsion away from it. If you have ever held two magnets near each other and felt the pull of attraction or push of repulsion between the two of them as they are placed closer and closer together, then you know what a force field feels like. There is a force between the two magnets that can't be seen but, nevertheless, can be perceived. On a much smaller scale, this is similar to the force field that exists in the smallest elements that make up an atom. If you think about this a minute, what we're saying is that if you take an object like the earth, break it down to its smallest indivisible parts that make up all its atoms, you are left with nothing but a bunch of very tiny force fields. If you could make these force fields stop vibrating or circling in their wave-type motions – in other words, stop their movement – they would cease to exist, since they're really nothing but the energy of movement anyway. As long as the smallest, indivisible parts of the atoms that make up the earth continue to move, the earth exists. If, for some reason, these smallest indivisible parts decided to stop moving, they would cease to exist, and the earth would also cease to exist. What makes these force fields exist in the first place, and how do they get started moving? These are questions that we are pretty sure we have the answers to, and they will be discussed in the section on quantum theory.

A more appropriate question, possibly, and one that relates all of this more directly to us would be – what would happen if we were not able to perceive a force field? The answer is that nothing would exist for us, not even our own bodies. Since matter is made of atoms, and atoms are made of tiny force fields that spin or vibrate, if we could not perceive the force fields, we could not be aware of them. This then means that we could not be aware of any matter composed of them either.

Let's look at what a perceivable object really is. We'll start with a heavy metal object, such as an anvil. If we look at it closer, we'll see that it is made of a bunch of tiny atoms of iron, arranged side by side and packed on top of each other. If we look even deeper at one of the individual atoms of iron that make up our anvil, we'll find that it has a nucleus made of several protons and neutrons. There will also be several electrons, which are made up of tiny force fields themselves, circling around the nucleus. If we go even deeper into the nucleus, we'll find that the protons and neutrons are further divided into quarks, and if we look deeper into a quark, we'll find nothing but force fields moving in some way, intertwined with other force fields, which hold them all together. You can picture this like the five intertwined circles that make up the International Olympics logo. If a force field wanted to somehow get away, it would have to break not only its own circular path, but also the paths of other force fields it is intertwined with as well. This would require a large addition of energy to accomplish, which is why the intertwining of these nuclear force fields is considered the strongest of all the forces found in nature. These force fields are the smallest "things" that objects can be broken down into. If we tried to break them down any further to something smaller, they would cease to exist as their motion would be interrupted.

The only reason we can perceive objects by additional means than just feeling an attraction or repulsion for them is because once these tiny little force fields are all put together to form atoms, then all the atoms are joined together to form objects, the force fields that make up these objects are so many in number and so tightly bound together that they become macroscopic in size to the point where all of our five senses can now function for perception. They become large enough to be impenetrable to such things as light, or the pressure receptors on the tips of our fingers. This means we can see them and touch them, respectively. As solid objects, they can bounce incoming light waves off themselves towards the receptors in our eyes, which makes them visible to us. As solid objects, they can also vibrate at certain frequencies, making them audible to our ears. If we could somehow make ourselves small enough to perceive individual force fields in atoms, we would see or hear nothing at all because we can't see or hear anything until there are enough force fields joined together to make a solid object that can bounce light rays or sound waves off it to the receptors in our eyes and ears. The larger objects that we can actually perceive with all five of our senses seem to be more "real" than the submicroscopic force fields that make them up.

It may sound strange that in order to perceive something as a real object (rather than just as an image, or hologram, of an object), even though we may be able to see it, we must, through our sense of touch, be able to perceive the submicroscopic force fields that make it up. The best way to explain this is by recalling what our sense of vision actually is. Remember that all we can perceive with our sense of vision is reflected light of various colors, not actual objects. When you look at something, you don't perceive that object, you perceive its color as reflected light. As we discussed in the first chapter, the receptors for vision in the eyes only respond to light energy, and that light energy has to be traveling at the exact frequency that can stimulate the receptors in the eyes to register in the brain as the various colors. If the frequency of the light waves is a little lower than what we can perceive in the visual range, we may feel them as infrared waves, but we won't see them as color because they can't stimulate the receptors in the eye to send an electrical impulse to the brain to register a visual perception. If the frequency of the light waves is a little higher than what we can perceive in the visual range, they may burn our skin as ultraviolet waves, but we will not be able to see them as color either. We can only perceive actual objects through our sense of touch. So, if we couldn't perceive a microscopic force field with our sense of touch, then putting trillions and trillions of them together so that they are large enough to bounce light rays towards our eyes in order that we can see them is not going to make them any more perceivable to our sense of touch as objects than if we couldn't see them. Only our sense of touch can determine if something is a real object for us or not because only our sense of touch can perceive the tiny force fields that ultimately make up matter.

There is a principle in the physics of very small things like force fields and electrons known as the Heisenberg uncertainty principle which states that you can never know the exact position of something like an electron, only its probable position. This is because when you try to measure its position, you change its characteristics. In other words, to measure its position at any given time, you'd have to stop it, but if you stopped it to make the measurement, it would cease to exist and there wouldn't be anything there to measure, since matter at these very small sizes is nothing but the energy of force fields that can only exist as long as they are moving.

Another phenomenon involving force fields is black holes. Black holes are created by the collapse of the space between the force fields that make up matter. Normally, an atom is mostly empty space, with the electrons moving around the nucleus of the atom at a relatively far distance from the nucleus. For instance, if the nucleus of an atom were the size of a basketball, the closest electrons moving around the nucleus would be about a mile away. In a black hole, the space between the force fields of the electrons and the force fields of the nucleus collapse to nearly zero. Even the space between the force fields that make up the protons and neutrons in the nucleus decreases. This can cause some impressive shrinking of the matter that contains these collapsing atoms. For instance, a planet the size of the earth could shrink to the size of a basketball, but still have the same number of atoms, and it would weigh the same as it did when it was the original earth size. Gravity in one of these black holes is so strong that not even light can escape its gravitational pull. This is why it's called a black hole. The interesting thing about a black hole, and the reason it applies to a discussion of energy and the brain is that once a black hole begins forming, nothing seems to be able to stop it from continuing to collapse until all the force fields in the atoms that make it up become so squashed together that they can't continue moving. What happens then is that at the center of the black hole, these force fields cease to exist as their movement is forced to stop. Complete planets that were perceivable to us are completely gone from existence, energy and all. Anything that happens to get near a black hole gets sucked into it because of its extreme force of gravity, and eventually will be compressed out of existence. The old maxim that states "energy can neither be created nor destroyed" is disproved in black holes, at least as far as our universe is concerned.

It should seem very strange that the human-sized objects we perceive by touching or viewing are ultimately made up of nothing but energy, or force fields, and that all of these force fields are nothing but moving pieces of "nothing." How can we perceive this "nothing" just because it's moving, and how can it even move at all if it's "nothing?" To explain this, let's go back to our two magnets. If we take two bar magnets and hold the south pole of one about a half inch from the north pole of the other, we will feel a force trying to pull the magnets together that requires a substantial effort on our part to equalize. There is nothing solid that we can touch or see that is pulling the magnets together. The only thing acting to pull the magnets together is the magnetic force field moving between the two magnets. Now let's take each of the magnets and beat them with a hammer a few times. If we then hold them a half-inch apart again, we find that there is no longer a magnetic force field between them, and we feel no resistance when we try to pull them apart. The force field has disappeared, or gone out of existence, and we can no longer perceive it. The force field between the two magnets never was an object, even though we could perceive it, and now it's still not an object and we cannot perceive it because its movement has stopped. You might wonder where the energy of movement in the force fields went. It was lost when we added a counteracting energy to the system by swinging the hammer at the magnets. In the case of the force fields that make up atoms and larger objects, an input of some kind of energy, such as from the intense gravity in a black hole, would also be required to stop the movement of the submicroscopic force fields, but that's not the point here. The point here is that there was a force field made out of "nothing" that we could perceive between the two magnets, and this force field became non-existent and non-perceivable when the movement of the force field between the two magnets was stopped. The force field existed because we could perceive it, even though it was made out of nothing. Once we could no longer perceive it, it stopped existing. What this means is that as humans, we can even perceive "nothing," as long as it is moving, which means it has energy to give off that can activate a receptor in one or more of our five senses, triggering an electric impulse that goes to our brain for analysis. To put it another way, we can perceive something as simple as pure energy, even though it's made of nothing, because energy is all that's required to stimulate a receptor for any of our five senses, and once that receptor is stimulated, it will then send an electric impulse to the brain to make us aware of it. If a receptor in the eye is stimulated by a "piece" of energy, then we will become aware of a visual perception. If a receptor at the tip of our finger is stimulated by the piece of energy, then we will be aware that something touched our finger, and so on. Theoretically, if one could artificially stimulate all the correct sensory receptors at the correctly timed speed sequence and location with some kind of an energy-producing machine, the person being stimulated would experience these perceptions as reality. When we discuss quantum theory and the origin of matter and energy, we will see that the only thing that really matters is what each of us perceives.

QUANTUM THEORY

Quantum physics can either be very difficult or somewhat easier to understand. If you try to understand it by working out the extremely sophisticated math equations that have been devised to describe it, it is impossible to understand. This is because quantum theory doesn't follow any of the math that we are accustomed to perceiving with our five senses. We would need at least a sixth, and maybe even a seventh, sense to perceive the math of quantum physics. If you forget about all the math that has been used to try to describe quantum physics, none of which has ever been proven to be an accurate explanation of the phenomena of quantum physics anyway, and try to understand just its concepts instead, it will become more clear.

As is the case with the force fields that make up matter, described in the previous section, in quantum theory, matter consists of moving force fields made of "nothing" too. Since this is usually a difficult concept to imagine, these force fields have often been described as a duality of a wave and a particle at the same time. That is, sometimes a "quantum" acts like a wave, and at other times it acts like a particle. It is unfortunate that it has been described as having this dual role just so that we can perceive it with the five senses we've got, because it has made the concept more difficult to understand, and this duality could not possibly exist anyway. There have been classic quantum experiments performed that give results showing that sometimes the force fields act like particles and sometimes they act like waves, depending on how the experiment is set up. This is why the duality nature was proposed as an interim way of describing quantum theory, even though we know that it can't be that way. The "double-slit" experiment, described next, demonstrates this.

All the mystery of quantum theory is contained in the double-slit experiment. This experiment has been duplicated numerous times with the same results. It consists of the following: A grid with two vertical slits is placed between a light source and a fluorescent screen. Light is then directed through both slits at the same time. The pattern that appears on the screen is one that shows alternating dark and light vertical bands, which is what you would expect to see if the light acted like waves, forming an interference pattern where the waves from one slit, when they meet the waves from the other slit, would either add or subtract from each other when they meet at the screen, showing bright or dark spots, respectively. This pattern is exactly what would be expected from light traveling through both slits at the same time if light traveled as waves. Next, one of the slits is closed off so that when the light is turned on, it can only go through one of the slits. The predicted pattern on the screen would normally be one bright spot directly behind the open slit, with a tapering in the brightness as one moved away from the center spot, if light truly was a wave form, as shown when both slits were open. However, the pattern on the screen is the same as when both slits are open, with alternating light and dark bands, even though there couldn't be an interference pattern with only one slit open. Even when the experiment is repeated with shooting just one photon of light at a time through the single slit, the interference pattern is still seen on the screen. Next a monitor is placed between the slit and the screen, in such a way that it doesn't interfere with the experiment itself, so that an observer can see exactly how the individual photons are able to give a seemingly impossible interference pattern while all going through the same slit. As soon as this monitor is placed, and an observer watches, the pattern on the screen changes from the interference alternating bands to a non-interfering single light band that grows dimmer away from the area behind the slit, as would be expected with no interference pattern. It has been shown beyond a doubt that putting the monitor there did not have anything mechanically to do with changing the pattern on the screen. The only explanation that physicists have been able to come up with for the phenomena observed is that the observer of the photons of light has actually changed the results of the experiment simply through the act of observing them. From this experiment and others along the same lines, it was deduced that we, and only we, can determine what exists. Another way to put this is that these types of experiments show that reality is created by the perceiver.

The premises of quantum theory include three main concepts. First, submicroscopic force fields do not move the same way that large matter moves. The submicroscopic force fields move in jumps from one point to another, rather than by gradually moving from one point to another. These are called quantum jumps. They occur in jumps because the orbit of a force field moving in a circular motion has to be a whole number of its wavelength. For instance, if one wavelength is three nanometers, then the orbit of that force field would have to measure out to some multiple of three nanometers, and if the force field were going to jump up to a more energetic orbit, it would have to increase its orbit by a multiple of three nanometers at a time instead of something like one or two nanometers at a time. It is also thought that the jump to another point is purely random. Second, the force fields cannot exist unless someone perceives them. This is somewhat akin to the tree falling in the forest making no sound unless someone is there to hear it. Third, there must be a new order in the universe that involves our brains as the ultimate determiners of what exists and what does not exist, at least at the submicroscopic level where force fields are found, since they can't exist unless someone perceives them. Not only does quantum theory suggest that the world only exists because it is being perceived by us, but that it can only change, at the quantum level, when it is not being perceived by us. While we're perceiving a submicroscopic force field, it can only exist the way we perceive it. Once we stop perceiving it, then it can change to a different position, for instance, or a different speed, and so on. This concept of quantum theory makes us seem pretty powerful. After all, it says that we are responsible for what goes on in a submicroscopic force field just by our act of perceiving it. The results of experiments, like the double-slit experiment described above, show this.

Quantum theory is a subjective theory, placing a premium on human perception as a definition of the existence of matter. It does not describe the objective properties of a physical system, but rather, the state of knowledge of the observer who probes it. In other words, as has been mentioned before, its premise is that nothing exists that we can't perceive. Quantum theory also says that the perception of quantum fields, or sub-microscopic force fields, is perceived differently by different people. For example, a quantum field can be thought of like a rainbow. A rainbow appears in a different place to different people, depending on where they are located. No two people see the exact same rainbow, even though it is real and can be perceived by anyone who looks at it. And equally important, it is not real unless it is being perceived, just like the force fields that make up matter in quantum theory. When we get to Part II, we will see some of the implications of this.

There has been an ongoing debate for many years about whether everything is predetermined by what has occurred before or whether things can truly occur randomly. Classical physics adopts the theory that what occurs in nature depends on what occurred before. In other words, everything is predetermined. For instance, all future events could be calculated in advance, using formulas and equations, if the initial motion of all the force fields in the atoms that make up everything that exists was known at some starting point. Through calculations, you would be able to predict exactly what you would be doing at a certain time ten years from now, since all motion of force fields must follow the laws of physics. In this way, you could predict the future. This is known as determinism. Quantum theory disagrees with this idea and says that more than one outcome is possible, even if you know what occurred previously, so you cannot predict where any specific force field will be in the future, no matter how many physics formulas you use. It says that cause and effect aren't rigidly linked, as they are in classical physics. Nothing is predetermined because what occurred previously has no effect on what occurs next, from a quantum viewpoint. This viewpoint of quantum theory is based on such things as the results obtained from the double-slit experiment described earlier, where the predicted result does not occur. Of course, this is far from proving that determinism is wrong. When we get to the chapter on choice in Part II, however, we will actually prove by two different methods that determinism can't exist.

One of the problems resulting from studying quantum theory on an experimental level is that most of the instruments used to measure quantum effects are of the classical physics variety. That is, quantum theory applies to the submicroscopic world, while the instruments used to measure what's going on at this small scale are of the macroscopic world – the world we perceive every day. When you use a macroscopic instrument to measure something on a submicroscopic scale, just the act of measuring what's going on can change the results. For instance, let's say you want to measure the energy generated by a photon, which is the smallest unit of light. In order for the photon to register on the device you would be using to measure its energy, some of the energy would be lost in triggering the measuring device. Since the energy of a photon is so small to begin with, any energy lost to trigger the measuring device would drastically change the amount of energy measured for the photon. All the devices we have to measure this very small field still require too much energy from what we're measuring to be very accurate. Fortunately, ingenious ways of getting around this problem have been devised, in some cases, so that this has not been an insurmountable problem.

ORIGIN OF MATTER

Where did everything come from? This is one of the most fascinating questions that has ever been pondered by man. It almost seems like the type of question there couldn't possibly be an answer for. After all, how can you make something out of nothing? We do have some pretty good ideas how matter originated, and there is good scientific research to back it up.

It has been shown in repeated studies that pairs of submicroscopic force fields can appear out of nothing in a vacuum, lead a brief existence, and then annihilate each other. Sometimes though, they don't destroy each other, and this results in the existence of new force fields in our universe. These new force fields are not derived from some other form of energy or anything else. They literally arise from nothing. Some scientists think that they may come from another dimension that we just can't perceive with our five senses, and are somehow transformed from force fields we can't perceive to force fields we can perceive. Although this may be a possibility, it doesn't matter for our purposes of saying that something arose from nothing, because for us, with our five senses for perceiving things, anything we can't perceive does not exist. As soon as it is transformed into something we can perceive, then it does exist. Nothing else matters. For instance, let's say we now have six senses and can perceive something that didn't exist in our "five senses" world. We would still be asking the same question – where did everything come from? Although we could perceive more force fields with our added sixth sense, the force fields we now perceived would still have had to originate from somewhere, just as they did when we only had five senses. Someone could then say that the force fields we now perceive with our six senses may have originated from an even higher dimension, and now we'd need a seventh sense to perceive that. As you can see, this could go on and on forever, adding more senses and more dimensions to perceive the origin of more and more new force fields. The point is that none of it matters. The only thing that matters is what we can perceive right now with the five senses we have right now. Anything that is going on in higher dimensions that we can't perceive has no meaning because it doesn't exist for us, and therefore, we can't interact with it.

There is another logical way we can tell that new force fields must arise out of nothing. Without continuous creation of new force fields from nothing, the universe must evolve towards a dead state in which all the matter in it condenses into a vast number of dead stars that eventually become black holes and disappear as they all burn out and get compressed into oblivion. Since we know that's not the case, because we wouldn't be here if it were, then we also know that new matter must originate from nothing to replace the "dead" matter that disappears in black holes.

Another method of showing that new force fields can arise from nothing involves the positive and negative energies of force fields and gravity. The energy of a gravitational field is negative, in the same sense that the energy of the force fields that make up matter is positive. It has been computed that the total amount of the positive energy of the force fields that compose matter is exactly countered by the amount of negative energy of the gravitational fields of all the matter in the universe. Therefore, the total energy in the universe is zero. Taking this one step further, since matter always has a gravitational force attached to it, and matter is composed of submicroscopic force fields, then each time a new force field arises out of nothing with its positive energy, it also brings with it a gravitational energy of an equal negative amount. The net gain of energy in the universe by the addition of a new force field is zero. So, even with the addition of something new in the universe for us to perceive, the universe itself is not "aware" of anything new being added because the positive and negative energies balance out. The only thing that's happened is that there are now more force fields that we can perceive in the universe because of some kind of transformation of a "nothing" that doesn't exist for us to a new "nothing" (a force field) that does exist for us. Remember that force fields are made of nothing, even though we can perceive them. So it appears again that the only thing that really changes is what we perceive, and since what we perceive is all that matters, we can say that new matter has truly arisen for us out of nothing.

GRAVITY

When we contemplate how the brain works, we probably don't put too much emphasis on the role gravity might play in this process. That would be a big mistake though. Gravity is very important to our perception of what's going on around us. In fact, gravity itself is something we can perceive. Every moment of our lives is spent under its influence. We even have specialized touch receptors for perceiving it. Some of them are in our inner ear for discerning whether we are right side up with respect to gravity, some are in our feet for feeling the pressure of the ground as gravity pulls us towards the earth, and some trigger our muscles to oppose the pull of gravity so we don't fall down when we're standing.

Gravity is associated with a negative energy, just as the submicroscopic force fields that make up matter are associated with a positive energy. When energy increases as new force fields come into existence, gravity also increases by an equal amount. This is so that the positive energy of new force fields is balanced with the negative energy of gravity. That way, no net change in energy occurs. When energy disappears from existence, such as when it is sucked into a black hole, gravity also disappears with it in equal amounts for the same energy conserving reasons. Why is gravity associated with being a negative energy while force fields that make up matter are associated with being a positive energy? There is no particular reason, any more than why one terminal of a battery is labeled positive and the other is labeled negative to denote the movement of current into and out of the battery. We know that the energy associated with gravity has to balance the energy associated with the force fields that compose matter, so one of them has to be positive and the other has to be negative. Without gravity, force fields and the matter they compose could not exist. There could be no addition of energy to the universe because there would be no way to balance it out to maintain a total energy of zero in the universe. Any energy that would be added by the spontaneous appearance of force fields would increase the overall energy of the universe, which cannot occur, because the net energy of the universe must remain at zero for the laws of physics to be obeyed. Why do the laws of physics have to be obeyed? If we can add energy at will, then all the laws of physics become meaningless and nothing would make any sense. It would be like pouring an ounce of water from one cup into another cup, then looking to see that there are now three ounces in the second cup, then looking again and seeing that there are now five ounces in the second cup. No physics laws would forbid this type of thing from occurring if the total positive energy of the universe could change at will. Added to this fact is that there is no way we could exist in this kind of a universe either.

According to Einstein, the force of gravity can't be real if it doesn't appear in all reference frames. If a change in the frame of reference makes gravity vanish, then it can't be a real force in the universe. He arrived at this conclusion about gravity when he realized that if a person is free-falling in a gravitational field, he cannot feel the effects of gravity in this frame of reference like he would if he were standing on the surface of the earth. In fact, he said that with your eyes closed, it would be impossible to tell the difference between free falling in a gravitational field and floating in place in deep outer space with no matter or energy around to exert a gravitational pull on you. Because of this, Einstein concluded that a gravitational field is not a field of force at all, but simply a curvature in the geometry of space.

The problem with this conclusion is one of perception. While in free-fall, versus while standing on the surface of the earth, one's perception of gravity changes, not the intrinsic force of gravity itself. In free fall, perception of gravity involves different touch receptors to perceive the force of gravity than while at rest. For instance, at rest, the anti-gravity muscles of the legs are used to perceive the force of gravity, and must be contracted to counteract this force. While in free-fall in a gravitational field, perception is by the various pressure receptors throughout the body that perceive the increasing speed of movement that the acceleration of gravity exerts. In this case, the anti-gravity muscles of the legs serve no purpose for perceiving gravity. Gravity is still present as a force in both cases, it's just perceived differently in each case.

Let's look at this change in perception of gravity from another aspect, where it's not movement in a gravitational field, but the at-rest location of a person in a gravitational field that affects how it is perceived. If it were possible to dig a hole all the way through the earth to the opposite side, a distance of about eight thousand miles, and you jumped into the hole, what would happen? You would accelerate at the rate of gravity until you reached the exact center of the earth, then you would decelerate at the same rate until you stopped, but would not quite reach the surface of the earth on the opposite side because of the slowing effect of the friction of the air. You would then accelerate in the opposite direction until you again reached the center of the earth. Then you would begin decelerating again. This moving back and forth would continue for some time until you finally stopped at the center of the earth. Once you were stopped at the center of the earth, you would no longer be accelerated by the force of gravity. You would be suspended in the center of the hole and would most likely perceive a sensation of being crushed as the force of gravity would be "pushing" on you equally from all directions, but you would not be accelerated in any direction, even though there would be no physical barrier keeping you from being moved. In this case, your perception of gravity while motionless in mid-air would be a crushing sensation, rather than the pulling sensation against the anti-gravity muscles in your legs if you were standing motionless on the surface of the earth. In other words, the gravitational force gives two completely different perceptions, depending on your location in space, relative to that gravitational force.

In order to make it a little clearer that it's not the "force" of gravity that changes with a change in the frame of reference, but our "perception" of gravity that changes with a change in the frame of reference, let's take it one step further to an extreme case. Suppose we have a person with no sense of touch. First we have him lie on the ground, and then we take him up in an airplane and go into a free-fall mode. Did he perceive gravity any differently in these two frames of reference? The answer is that he did not. He didn't perceive gravity at all in either case because he doesn't have the sense of touch required to perceive it. He may have floated out of his seat when the plane went into free-fall, but he didn't feel any gravitational forces acting on him in either case. He probably knows that if he jumps off a building, he will go downwards and will probably die at impact, but he does not feel the force of gravity pulling him towards the earth when he jumps. He cannot perceive gravity by actively experiencing it. He can only know about it through passive perceptions from someone else via language. In his case, the frames of reference are equivalent, whether he is in free-fall or sitting on the ground. Since they are equivalent, then this would appear to contradict the conclusion that a gravitational field is not a field of force at all, but simply a curvature in the geometry of space.

Getting back to the original Einstein premise mentioned above, which states that a person floating freely in space with no matter or energy around to exert any force on him would feel no different than someone free-falling in a gravitational field, it should now be more clear that the person free-falling in a gravitational field would certainly feel something that the person floating freely in space would not feel. The person free-falling in the gravitational field would perceive the acceleration of gravity in his specialized touch receptors that are designed for detecting acceleration, while the person floating freely in space would not, since he is not being accelerated. Therefore, these two situations are not the same, but different, and this difference is due to human perception. Perception is always what is central to us as humans, because it is what makes us who we are. Assigning a gravitational field to a curvature of space has been shown to work out very well mathematically, but as we've seen in the previous chapter, math does not always deal with what exists for us in our reality, even when the results are mathematically logical. In the final analysis, it's what we perceive that determines what exists for us, and the reason is because we are limited by the five senses we have, whereas, math equations are not limited by *any* senses.

Gravity affects anything that is made of energy or matter, either of which can be converted into the other. This is why light, which is made of pure energy, is bent towards a gravitational field, such as a planet, as it passes by. The fact that gravity is attractive means that it will tend to draw the matter in the universe together to form objects like stars and planets. These large accumulations of matter can support themselves for a time against further contraction under the influence of gravity because as they become compressed under the force of gravity, an intense heat, or thermal pressure, is created which tends to push them back apart. However, once the thermal pressure burns out, then gravity will gradually take over and compress the burned out sun or planet more and more until it becomes a black hole which, as we saw earlier, eventually ceases to exist altogether when the force fields that make it up are compressed so tightly that they stop moving. Once they stop moving, they cease to exist.

We have seen that in the very small-scale world of quantum mechanics, the submicroscopic force fields that make up everything we perceive are dominant. However, in our large-scale world, gravity is the dominant force. Because of this, we have several different types of modified touch receptors to perceive gravity. Much of what we know about gravity is due to theoretical physics, using mathematical formulations to arrive at workable conclusions about gravity. In the end, though, it's what we actually perceive about gravity that is important.

THE BIG BANG

There are several questions regarding our universe that scientists are still trying to find the answers to, including how the universe was created, whether it is infinite in its dimensions, and why it was all created in the first place. You may wonder what this has to do with our discussion of how the brain works. Since we are made from the same materials that formed all matter, it should be interesting to know some of the various theories about how the force fields that eventually formed us arose out of nothing. There are a few models that have been proposed to explain how everything began. The "big bang" model has been in vogue for the past thirty to forty years, so it will be the primary model we will discuss in this section.

In the steady-state model, the universe has neither a beginning nor an end. It goes on forever. As various galaxies of stars and planets die out and become black holes, eventually ceasing to exist altogether, new force fields arise out of nothing to form new matter to replace it all, as mentioned previously.

According to the big bang model, all the galaxies and other matter that exist in the universe were spawned out of one force field that arose from nothing about fourteen billion years ago. As soon as the first force field came into existence, it immediately mushroomed into many more force fields, which then formed the matter that makes up planets, stars, and everything else that exists in the universe today.

One of the problems with the big bang model is that if everything was spawned from one force field at one time, but this is not continuing to occur over and over, then the universe should be dying out now as all the fuel that arose with the big bang is burning out. More importantly, this model would have to explain why the laws of physics were completely different when the big bang occurred than they were after all the matter was created. The reason the laws of physics would have to be different now is because, according to the current laws of physics, every reaction results in less order in the universe after that reaction than existed before it occurred. In other words, overall order in the universe decreases with every reaction. At the beginning of the big bang, just the opposite would have had to occur, because more order existed after every reaction until all the matter in the universe was created. Proponents of the big bang model feel that the laws of physics were actually different when the first force field came into existence, but within a short time after all the matter in the universe started forming, the laws of physics changed to what they are now. As you might imagine, there are a lot of scientists who would prefer a theory that doesn't allow the laws of physics to change, no matter what's going on. Added to this is the fact that if the rate of expansion of the single force field into all the matter that evolved from it during the beginning of the big bang had occurred one millionth of a millionth of a second slower or faster, the universe would not exist today. Of course, the answer to this dilemma is that if the universe didn't exist today, we wouldn't be here to talk about it, so it doesn't matter how close the tolerances, time-wise, had to be. The point of this, though, is that the steady state model does not require all these close tolerances for us to be here.

One of the biggest attractions for the big bang model is that it meshes well with religious beliefs in that it supposes a specific point in time that everything was created. This fact has gained a lot of support for the big bang model from religious officials. The steady state model does not square well with religious beliefs because its premise is that the universe was always there and matter is constantly being created out of nothing at the same time that matter is also being constantly destroyed in black holes.

The big bang model takes what exists now, and then extrapolates backward to determine how it all must have started at the beginning. This presents more problems. For example, let's say I am going to fly from New York to Los Angeles and it will take ten hours. If I wanted to determine how fast the plane is going to be flying, I might divide the three thousand mile distance between the two cities by ten hours to arrive at an average airspeed of three hundred miles per hour. However, what if the plane has to stop in Atlanta for four hours along the way before going on to Los Angeles? Then the average air speed is closer to five hundred miles per hour. Without knowing what's going on between the beginning and the end of a journey, there's no way to know for sure what happened from one point in time to another. If you'll recall our discussion of quantum theory, this is one of its major premises. That is, we can't know for certain what occurred prior to what we are observing right now.

The final problem that plagues the big bang model is that none of what has been proposed to have occurred in the big bang model has ever been able to be reproduced or proven in an experimental lab. On the contrary, the steady state model has been shown to be a workable model in the experimental lab.

THE THEORY OF EVERYTHING

There are four natural forces found in the universe. Three of these forces apply to individual atoms and their nuclei. The strongest of these three forces is the one that holds the individual submicroscopic force fields together. The weakest of these three is the force that tends to allow larger nuclei of atoms to break into smaller nuclei, such as what occurs when Uranium atoms are split into two smaller atoms plus a lot of energy when an atomic bomb is set off. The third is the electromagnetic force that keeps electrons spinning around the nucleus of an atom instead of flying off into space. The fourth natural force is gravity. Gravity is, by far, the weakest of all four forces and, as we've seen previously, is responsible for attracting all matter or energy to any other matter or energy in its vicinity. Physicists have been trying for over a hundred years to come up with a set of formulas that will tie all four of these forces together, and have not been able to succeed. At the current time, the equations used in quantum theory explain and predict the forces that exist at the submicroscopic levels quite well, while the equations devised by Einstein for general relativity explain and predict the forces that exist on the large scale quite well. The problem is that neither quantum theory nor relativity theory will work for both the small and large-scale forces. This does not sit well with physicists, because there should be a single law of physics that can account for what happens on both the small and large scale, rather than having separate laws for each. For Einstein, because general relativity didn't explain quantum theory, he felt that relativity theory could only be a step toward his goal, which was to find a theory of quantum phenomena that would agree with all the experiments and satisfy his demand for clarity and completeness.

At the current time, "string" theory is in vogue as a possible explanation of all four forces. String theory is strictly a math exercise, rather than one based on perception, as it requires not just our usual three dimensions to work, but as many as ten dimensions. Although it might eventually be found to work out mathematically to unite all four natural forces, there is probably no way we could ever perceive something like this with our mere five senses. In this case, the cutting edge of physics and math has left reality far behind.

Since the mating of quantum theory with relativity theory has not been done yet, in spite of a hundred years of so many math and physics scientists working on it, it's most likely because either the whole approach is wrong, in that they are trying to work it out using pure math rather than something involving perception, or we may not have an adequate base for perceiving what is necessary to figure out this problem. That is, we may require a sixth or seventh sense to be able to understand how to put it all together.

SUMMARY

In this chapter, we've discussed where everything that we can perceive originates, and that nothing exists unless we can perceive it. We also saw that what we perceive is made from nothing, but exists because we are able to perceive that "nothing", as long as it is moving. We also saw that there are ideas in physics that we will continue to be unable to prove because of our only having five senses. Even our math, which we've seen can go beyond our five senses to solve problems, may not be enough to solve some of these problems.

WHO ARE WE, REALLY?

LIGHT

Light is one of the strangest phenomena that we perceive. We can't hold it in our hands, yet we can stop it by putting our hand in its path. It has been shown to exhibit both a wave-like nature and a particle-like nature at times, even though it can't be both. Einstein, who is most famous for his theories on relativity, did not receive his Nobel Prize for relativity. He received it for his work with light, by showing that when light hits an object, its energy can knock an electron loose from that object. Without light, photosynthesis could not take place and we would have nothing to eat and no air to breathe. Because of the specialized receptors for light in our eyes, we can perceive things far beyond what we can touch and hear. Most of the memories stored in our brains are visual, resulting from the perception of light. In this chapter, we will look at what light is, where it comes from, why its speed is so important, and how we could theoretically visualize events that occurred years ago, just as if they were happening now, by manipulating light.

ORIGIN OF LIGHT

How does a light wave originate and get started moving? Light is an electromagnetic wave that is made of pure energy that just happens to be able to trigger the receptors in the back of our eyes to send an electric impulse to the brain in order to register as something perceived visually. It is similar in consistency to the submicroscopic force fields mentioned in the previous chapter, but instead of staying bound up in the nucleus of the atom, circling round and round or vibrating back and forth, it is released from the atom as a tiny loss of the overall energy of that atom, either because that atom absorbed some incoming energy from somewhere else and now wants to get rid of it, or because the atom is decaying. If a light wave is broken down into the smallest "piece" of energy it is made of, this smallest piece of light is called a photon. If one light source appears brighter to our eyes than another light source, it is because the brighter light source is simply giving off more photons. When a photon is released from an atom, it travels in a straight line forever unless it is either absorbed by an atom in some object it contacts, increasing that object's total energy, or is bent by a gravitational field it passes, or is reflected in a different direction off an object that can't absorb it.

You might wonder how the photon being released from an atom could ever pack enough energy to travel on and on forever without using all its energy up in the process and fizzling out to nothing along the way. It was discovered over a hundred years ago that when an electric field is first generated, such as when you turn on an electric switch, or when the electric field is first released as energy from an atom, as in the case of our photon, it triggers a magnetic field at a right angle to the direction the electric field started. It was also discovered that when a magnetic field first starts out, it triggers an electric field at a right angle to the direction the magnetic field started. As an example of this phenomenon, you can take a loop of electrical wire that is connected to an amp meter that registers any flow of electricity in it, hold the electrically dead loop of wire steady in one hand, then take a bar magnet and quickly pass it into the loop of electric wire with your other hand. The amp meter gauge attached to the loop of wire will show that an electric current was generated in the loop of wire just from passing the bar magnet through the loop of wire. The same thing occurs in our photon being released from an atom. As the photon is released, it is changing from nothing to an electric charge being dispelled by the atom. When this occurs, it triggers a magnetic field at a right angle to this new electric charge. Then, as the new magnetic field forms, it triggers a new electric field at a right angle to the magnetic field, which then triggers another new magnetic field, which then triggers another new electric field, and so on. This goes on forever without stopping because each change in electric or magnetic field actually creates a *new* magnetic or electric field at right angles to the previous magnetic or electric field. This results in a saw-tooth shaped wave that is self-propagating away from the original source in a straight line. The original piece of energy that started all this fizzled out way back near the atom where it started, just after it triggered the first magnetic wave to form, but each change from electric to magnetic field or magnetic to electric field regenerates the energy of the photon that is moving forever in a straight line. The electric and magnetic fields take on an independent existence, once they get started, no longer associated with what got them started, because of this unusual relationship between changing electric and magnetic fields. This is why these waves are called "electromagnetic" waves. The fact that each changing electric or magnetic field in sequence forms at right angles to its counterpart results in the electromagnetic wave always moving in a straight line.

The self-propagation of electromagnetic waves creates some strange effects. When Einstein was working out his theory of relativity, he discovered that the speed of light, or the speed of any electromagnetic wave, was measured at the same rate, 186,000 miles per second, no matter what the frame of reference happened to be. What this means is that if you happened to be moving towards the sun at a speed of one half the speed of light, and you measured the speed of light waves in your frame of reference coming towards you from the sun, you would measure them at their usual 186,000 miles per second, not one and a half times that speed. The reason for this is that because electromagnetic waves are self-propagating, they are not dependent on their source to continue traveling through space. Also, because they are self-propagating, they don't require a universal medium to carry them along. For instance, when sound travels from its source to where someone hears it, the air carries the sound waves. If you happen to be moving closer to the origin of the sound, then you will also be moving relative to the air that carries the sound, and the speed of the sound waves you hear will be increased by the speed you are traveling towards them. Since light waves don't need a medium to travel through space, the speed and direction of movement of the frame of reference that you happen to be in when the light waves reach you from some other frame of reference don't matter. You will measure the speed of the incoming light waves the same no matter whether you are moving towards them or away from them. The fact that light waves are self-propagating means that once they are initiated at their starting point, which in this case is the sun, they don't rely on the sun for continued movement through space. This further means that your movement relative to the sun no longer matters either, because the sun is no longer a frame of reference for the light waves once they leave it. It would be like the light waves whose speed you are measuring had no specific origin once they left the sun, so when they arrive in your frame of reference, that would be the equivalent of being their starting point. Since any frame of reference they enter becomes the equivalent of a new starting point for them, because of their self-propagation, their speed will always be measured the same in any frame of reference, no matter how fast or in which direction that frame of reference happens to be moving. (We will be discussing frames of reference in more detail later in the chapter on relativity.)

Why don't the submicroscopic force fields that make up the nucleus of the atom continually send out electromagnetic waves? After all, they're moving energy fields too. The reason they don't send out electromagnetic waves is because these force fields are not *changing* force fields. They are moving continuously, but they are not stopping and starting. It is the stopping or starting of an energy field that creates an electromagnetic wave.

There is nothing special about the electromagnetic waves we see as light, except that they happen to have a wavelength that is not too small and not too large to trigger the receptors in our eyes for notifying the brain that we are seeing something.

Electromagnetic waves don't all have the same amount of energy. The more energy the electromagnetic wave starts out with, the faster the switching will be from electric field to magnetic field, or from magnetic field to electric field. The faster the switch from one field to the other, the shorter each sawtooth wave, or wavelength, will be. The electromagnetic waves with the most energy and shortest wavelengths are x-rays and gamma rays, both of which are so much higher in energy than light waves that they can pass right through our bodies. In fact, as they pass through our bodies, if they happen to hit one of the atoms in our DNA, they have enough energy that they can knock part of it out so that it's no longer the way it's supposed to be. This can cause the DNA to behave strangely, coding for the wrong proteins, or not turning off production when it's supposed to. This can result in too much production of something in our bodies, as occurs when cancer results from exposure to gamma waves or x-rays.

The electromagnetic waves that are just slightly more energetic than the ones in the upper limits of our visual range are the ultraviolet waves. Their wavelengths are shorter than purple light, so we can't see them. They don't have enough energy to go all the way through our bodies, but they are able to go through the upper layers of our skin, which is why they cause sunburns. They do have enough energy to disrupt the DNA located in our skin cells though, and that is why they can cause skin cancer in those people who spend too much time in the sun.

Electromagnetic waves in the visible spectrum don't have enough energy to cause disruption in our DNA, so they don't cause cancer. On the lower end of the energy curve for electromagnetic waves, lower in energy than the lowest of the visible range, are infrared waves and radio waves, such as AM and FM waves. Since these have relatively long wavelengths and are lower in energy than the electromagnetic waves in the visible range, they don't usually disrupt DNA either.

Because light waves are made of energy, and energy and matter are interchangeable, light should be attracted by gravity, just as all matter is. This has been shown by experiment to be the case. When light from a distant star travels past our sun, for example, on its journey towards the earth, it is bent towards the sun by a predictable amount along its pathway, due to the gravity of the sun.

THE SPEED OF LIGHT

Light travels at a speed of about 186,000 miles per second. Actually, all electromagnetic waves travel at this speed, whether they are high-energy x-ray waves, low energy radio waves, or the in-between light waves we are able to perceive with our sense of vision. By convention, this speed that all the various types of electromagnetic waves travel at is referred to as the "speed of light" rather than the "speed of electromagnetic waves," probably because visible light is the predominant type of electromagnetic radiation that we perceive.

Einstein determined a hundred years ago that the speed of light was the fastest that anything could travel. What is so special about the speed of light being the universal speed limit? It's not so much that nothing can travel faster than the speed of light, but rather that no *information* can travel faster than the speed of light that makes this speed so important. When you think about the fastest possible ways that we can receive information, they all depend on electromagnetic waves to transmit that information. Radios, television, telephone, our visual perception, and anything else you can possibly think of rely on electromagnetic waves for transmission of information from somewhere else to our brain. If something could go faster than the speed of light, there's no way we would know about it because we have no sensory receptors for perceiving anything that travels faster than light. Any information traveling faster than light waves would not be perceivable by our eyes or any of our other senses and would therefore not exist for us. To make the transmission of information at the speed of light a little more clear, let's say the sun suddenly burned out. Would we know about this as soon as it occurred? The answer is that we would not. The reason is because the light waves coming to us from the sun travel at 186,000 miles per second, and the sun is 93,000,000 miles away. By dividing this out, we find that it would take around eight minutes from the time the sun burned out until the last bit of light that left the sun before it burned out reached us. There is absolutely no possible way we could ever know about the sun burning out before eight minutes after it actually occurred. Even if someone could somehow be sufficiently close to the sun so that he would see it burn out immediately, there is no way he could signal us here on earth that the sun had burned out any faster than eight minutes after it actually burned out. This is because he would have to communicate this information to us using some form of electromagnetic waves, and they would also require the same eight minutes of time to reach the earth since all electromagnetic waves travel at the speed of light.

Now, let's suppose that instead of the sun suddenly burning out, the earth suddenly begins to speed away from the sun in the opposite direction at a speed slightly faster than the speed of light. Once the earth's speed away from the sun surpassed the speed of light, if someone standing on the earth were looking back at the sun, he suddenly would see nothing where the sun used to be. This is because the earth is now moving away from the light waves coming from the sun faster than those light waves are moving towards the earth. Consequently, those light waves from the sun would never be able to reach the earth, so they could not strike the receptors in the back of his eyes and he could not perceive that light from the sun. Everything would appear dark on the earth. Someone might object to this, saying that maybe we could still see the light coming from the sun back in the distance, even though that light will never catch up to us. The answer to this is to remember that our sense of vision doesn't "see" anything, including light waves traveling through space, unless they are reflected off something or hit the receptors in the back of our eyes directly in their straight-line path from the sun. Since there is no actual sunlight reaching our eyes because the earth is moving away from the sun faster than the light waves can travel towards the earth in our example, there's no way to see anything "back in the distance." Even if a light wave from the sun were one inch away from our eyes, but the earth was moving at slightly greater than the speed of light away from the sun, that light wave one inch away from our eyes could never be perceived because it would never reach the light receptors in the back of our eyes. For us, that light wave does not exist.

There is nothing special about the speed of light being around 186,000 miles per second. That just happens to be the speed at which the electric and magnetic force fields alternately propagate themselves as they leave an atom. If they could propagate themselves along in their saw tooth fashion any faster or any slower, they would.

According to Einstein's famous formula that equates the energy of an object to its mass times the speed of light squared, as the object's speed increases, its energy increases, and if its energy increases, then its mass increases. This formula further predicts that once an object is moving at the speed of light, its mass is infinitely large. Since this is impossible, it means that no object could ever have enough energy to move at the speed of light. Earlier, it was mentioned that if something could go faster than the speed of light, there's no way we would ever know about it because we have no sensory receptors for perceiving anything that travels faster than light. You may have thought about the possibility of something like a rock moving at a speed faster than the speed of light which, if it contacted us, would certainly be perceived most painfully through our sense of touch. Now you can see why this is an impossibility. If the rock were moving at the speed of light, or faster than the speed of light, its mass would have to be infinite in order to match the energy it had at that speed, and this is impossible. However, if it were possible for something that had no mass, like a very tiny force field of pure energy, to move faster than the speed of light, it would pass right through our bodies without our ever being aware of it, since none of our various sensory receptors have the capacity to perceive anything moving faster than the speed of light. So, in summary, we can say with certainty that nothing can go faster than the speed of light, but if something could, it wouldn't matter anyway because we couldn't perceive it. The reasons are because any solid object would have an infinite mass at the speed of light, which is impossible, and because anything small enough to have no mass while moving faster than the speed of light would not be able to be perceived by us anyway. This means it wouldn't exist for us. (It should be mentioned that through theoretical math, particles called tachyons have been predicted that can exceed the speed of light. As you may recall, math isn't always consistent with our reality, and this is probably the case in this instance, given that nothing moving faster than the speed of light can exist for us.)

Although electromagnetic waves can be perceived by our other senses as well as by our eyes as light – for instance, infra-red electromagnetic waves are perceived by our touch receptors as heat – it is our sense of vision, by far, that is the most important perceptual device for electromagnetic waves. Without our sense of vision, we would know nothing of the universe outside of our own immediate environment. We could still feel the warmth of the sun from the infrared electromagnetic waves it radiated towards the earth, but we would have no idea that the warmth we feel came from somewhere other than the air in our immediate surroundings.

Scientists have wondered what the universe would look like from a photon's viewpoint. For instance, if it were possible to "ride on a photon," what would the universe look like from this vantage point? Some scientists have predicted that from the photon's viewpoint, everything else would appear to be rushing past it at the speed of light while the photon just sits there in space. Although this may or may not be true, it really doesn't make any difference because the only thing that matters is what we perceive in our own frame of reference through our five senses and our brain. For instance, photons can't be aware of space, time, or anything else, so there is no looking at the universe from a photon's viewpoint. Because we *do* have the ability to perceive what goes on in the universe, what occurs in space or time only has meaning for us in our own frame of reference as humans with brains.

Astronomers deal with extremely large distances. In order to keep from having to use lots of zeros when writing out distances, they use the term "light years" to denote the distance from one place to another in space. A light year is the distance in miles that a light wave travels in one year, and is equal to about six trillion miles. When astronomers look through their telescopes at a star that is a million light years away from us, the light they are now seeing would have had to leave that star one million years ago. So what the astronomers are seeing when they look in the telescope is not what's going on with that star right now, but what was going on with that star one million years ago, because of the one million light years of time it took the light leaving the star to finally arrive here at the earth. If they had a telescope that could view objects fourteen or fifteen billion light years away, about the time that the big bang would have taken place, they could see if the big bang actually did take place, because the light that originated at the distance of fourteen or fifteen billion light years from earth would now just be reaching us.

The fact that light travels at a finite speed means that we can look at events that took place in the past on distant planets and stars. But this finite speed of light also implies that we can look at events that have taken place on earth in the past as well. For instance, when the atomic bomb was dropped on Hiroshima in 1945, the light from this explosion radiated out into space at 186,000 miles per second. If it were possible to get in a space ship and fly off at several times the speed of light, you could eventually reach the light from the explosion traveling through space and witness the explosion, just as if you were watching it as it occurred. Of course, we already know that we can't get in a spaceship and fly off at greater than the speed of light because nothing can go faster than the speed of light. However, remember that light can be bent by gravity so, if on its pathway through space after leaving the explosion of the atomic bomb in Hiroshima in 1945, the light waves are continually bent by a gravitational force to the right, for example, eventually they would go in a circular pathway and could possibly end up back at the earth. Someone looking in a telescope may happen to be looking out into space at just the right time when the light is returning from that 1945 bomb blast and see it occur, just as if he were watching it in 1945. Remember that for something visual to be perceived, all that has to happen is that light waves have to enter the eye and energize the receptors for light in the back of the eye, which then send electrical impulses to the brain where the viewer then becomes aware of the perception.

SUMMARY

Light is the only thing that powers our sense of vision. If it reaches our eyes, we can be made aware of the existence of objects that are beyond our immediate grasp. Once a light wave is emitted from an object, it is self-propagating. Although light waves move extremely fast, their speed is not infinite. This has been shown to present some interesting situations where occurrences from the past can be perceived in the present. While the speed of light is not infinite, it does appear to be the universal speed limit. Nothing can go faster than the speed of light.

TIME

Time is one of the most discussed topics in history. Philosophers were discussing it over two thousand years ago, and in more modern times, physicists are discussing it too. It has been described at various times as a concept, a percept, an illusion, and the fourth dimension. In this chapter, we will discuss what time is, how the brain deals with time, and what purpose time serves in the functioning of our brain.

WHAT IS TIME

First of all, let's answer one of the most debated questions about time – is time an illusion? The answer is that time is certainly not an illusion. An illusion is something that is perceived differently than how we know it actually exists because our senses are not infallible in all situations. What determines that something is an illusion is that when we perceive it, and the perception of it enters our brain via one of our five senses to be compared to other memories of similar perceptions, we come to the conclusion that what we are perceiving can't exist as we perceive it, based on those previous memories of similar perceptions or on further perceptions about it that show it to be an illusion. For instance, when we're driving through the desert on a very flat stretch of pavement, we look down the road in the distance and see that the road has been replaced by a large body of shining water. As we continue driving, we see that when we reach the area where we thought the road had been replaced by the body of water, it turns out to have been just a reflection. The next time we see this same phenomenon, when that perception of the water triggers the receptors in the back of our eyes to send an electric impulse to the brain for comparison with similar memories, we will conclude that what we are seeing is an illusion, not a body of water, and that the road is not washed out ahead. For time to be an illusion, we'd have to have stored memories of previous perceptions of non-illusory time for comparison to determine that our senses were playing tricks on us when perceiving the "illusory" time. To have stored memories of perceptions of time in our brains to compare the illusory version to would mean that time is something we can perceive through our five senses because we'd have to perceive it to store memories of it. Having stored memories of time would prove that all time is not illusory, but that it is at least occasionally perceivable with one or more of our five senses. You can't know that something is an illusion when you perceive it unless you've got prior knowledge from previous memories of perceptions to compare it to in order to draw the conclusion that it's not real. If you don't have any previous perceptions for comparison, then there's no way you could know it was an illusion when you first perceive it. Also, since an illusion is still a perception, albeit a wrong perception, then we would, in effect, be saying that time can be a real perception, but in some cases, it can be a wrong perception. In other words, to use the term "illusion" to refer to time in general, one would have to mean that there is a perceivable time, but all perceivable time is an illusion. As you can see, this would make no sense. It would be like saying that something can exist without existing.

We've shown why time can't be an illusion, but in the explanation, it was sort of implied that time was a perception. Could time be a perception? The answer is that time can't be a perception either. A perception is something we are aware of through one or more of our five senses. Since there is no way we can see, touch, hear, smell, or taste time, time cannot be a perception. We can perceive a clock, of course, but a clock is not "time". A clock is only an object that measures time. (We will discuss time as a measuring tool shortly.)

Could time be the fourth dimension? The three dimensions we are familiar with, including height, width, and depth, are perceivable by definition. That is, they refer to characteristics of objects that we can be aware of through our five senses. Since time does not refer to a perceivable characteristic of an object, it cannot be a dimension.

We've eliminated everything that time has been purported to be except the possibility that time is a concept. A concept is a memory formed in the brain that is generated completely within the brain itself, using memories that exist in the brain as a starting point, either of perceptions or other conceptions, then modifying them to produce a completely new memory that is not exactly like any of those used to generate it. In contrast, memories formed in the brain of perceptions are usually recorded unchanged, just as they are perceived (except for minor modifications needed to make them less cumbersome to recall, as stated in a previous chapter). For instance, we may read about an auto manufacturer coming out with a "concept" car. This is an appropriate name for this type of car because the person who designs it has memories of conventional cars in his brain, but he changes various things in his brain about these memories of conventional cars and draws a picture of a completely different-appearing car that looks nothing like any of the conventional cars on the road. He had received no perception of the exact car he designed, but he modified the memories of perceptions of conventional cars he'd seen in the past to come up with new memories that were completely different from any memories of cars he had ever seen, or perceived. In this case, the new design is the result of a concept in his brain. To be more accurate with our description in this example, the concept car is only a concept when it is in the car designer's brain. Once he draws it out on paper or it is built, it is no longer a concept but perceivable, either by viewing the drawing on the paper or the built car itself. Conceptions, by definition, can't be perceived, or they would be perceptions instead.

Although we've mentioned that time has been purported to be an illusion, the fourth dimension, a percept, and a concept at various times, there are really only two possibilities for what time can actually be, as far as we humans with brains are concerned. Time either has to be a percept or a concept. If it were anything else, there's no way we could ever be aware of it. This is because our brain only deals with, and is aware of, things that are perceived and thoughts that are conceived. Nothing else exists or matters for our brain. In other words, if there's no way you can perceive it or conceive it, there's no possible way you can know about it, which also means there's no way you can interact with it. Someone might object to this by saying that there are things in the atmosphere, like pollen, chemicals, and even cosmic rays and other electromagnetic waves from outer space that affect us all the time, and we aren't aware of all these. However, we actually do perceive all these things through our various senses. Cosmic rays can be recorded by instruments that we can then listen to or visualize on a video screen. Pollen causes a reaction in our nose via the sense of touch and may cause us to sneeze, and so on. If any of these things cannot be perceived by any means available to us, ultimately via our five senses, then they don't exist for us. It's as simple as that. So it appears that since time is obviously something we are aware of, it has to exist for us, and if it exists, but cannot be perceived, then it must be a concept.

TIME AND THE BRAIN

If time is a concept rather than a percept, then it only exists within the confines of our brain. And if it only exists within our brain, there should be a reason for this – after all, evolution usually selects against things that don't serve a purpose. In this case, there is a very good reason why time is essential to our survival. You may recall from a previous chapter that when a perception triggers a receptor from one of our five senses to fire an electric signal, it sends the electric signal to the brain for comparison with other memories in the brain similar to that new perception to determine a correct response to the new perception. If we had no concept of the flow of time, then our stored memories could not have been stored with a time line either, and there is no way we could accurately compare a memory of a previous perception to an incoming new perception in order to effect the appropriate response. The recalled memories of previous perceptions would be recalled in a jumbled up way, rather than according to a time line. For instance, suppose you're out in the jungle and a wild boar approaches you. You immediately find a tree and climb up into it. You then take your cell phone out of your pocket and call someone to come and rescue you. The reason you knew what to do is because you have stored memories of similar perceptions in your brain that this new perception of the boar approaching you were compared to in order to determine the appropriate response. The stored memories were filed along a time line when they were first recorded so that you would know the sequence of actions you should perform to get away from the wild boar. Now let's suppose that the previous memories of similar perceptions to the wild boar approaching you had not been recorded in your memory banks along a time line. You might then recall from that memory of similar perceptions that you need to get out your cell phone and call someone to rescue you and that you need to go climb a tree to get away from the wild boar but you wouldn't know what the order of these two responses should be. Since your previous memories of similar perceptions are what determine your response, and they weren't recorded along a time line, you could just as likely recall the memory to get out your cell phone and call for someone to rescue you first, and then go climb up a tree, rather than climbing the tree first. The result would be that the wild boar would overpower you while you were standing there dialing your cell phone. So, from an evolutionary standpoint, it is essential that perceptions be recorded along the same time line as they were originally received.

The feeling we have of time "flowing" is entirely due to the way the formation of memories proceeds, incorporating a conceptual flow of time with each train of perceptions that reaches the brain so that when the memory of that perception sequence is recalled, the time line along which it was formed will enable us to recall it from memory as a time-ordered perception.

Types of Time

It is extremely unfortunate that the term "time" has been used to describe two completely different things, and therefore we need to label and define them differently. The two types of time are "objective" time and "subjective" time. When the two types of time are used interchangeably, it becomes very frustrating for philosophers, physicists, and everyone else to describe exactly what time is. We end up reading passages in books such as "time doesn't exist," or "time is just an illusion," or "time is the fourth dimension." We can now clarify what the two types of time are, how each functions separately from the other, and try to clear up the controversy about time.

Objective time is a measurement and nothing more. Pure objective time is used for solving math and physics problems. Examples of objective time might be "ten seconds," "three years," "1947," "1850 to 1875," and so on. As a type of "time," it cannot be perceived or conceived, so it doesn't exist for us – as time. For instance, the term "twenty minutes" means nothing to us as pure time. If someone says, "I'll meet you in twenty minutes," we don't perceive a flow of time of twenty minutes. Our brain doesn't have that capacity. We can only perceive what our five senses allow, and twenty minutes can't be seen, touched, heard, tasted, or smelled. We also can't conceive

147

twenty minutes either. A conception requires recalling memories from the brain that were originally formed from perceptions, then changing them in such a way that a new memory can be made that is different from the original memory. Since we can't perceive twenty minutes, there's no way we can store it as a perception to be modified by conception, so conception of objective time as "time" doesn't exist either. The way we deal with objective time is by perceiving and conceiving it as "distance," or "space" because these are things that we *can* perceive or conceive. When someone says, "I'll meet you in twenty minutes," we might perceive the twenty minutes by recalling from working memory a clock, and we then might picture the big hand moving from twelve down to four, a "space" of twenty minutes. Or we might recall from working memory what we can do for that twenty minutes, comparing perceptions of things we've done in the past during that time period, adding them up so that we arrive at the number of things we can do that will take twenty minutes. Or we may just sit and do nothing, occasionally looking at our wristwatch to monitor the twenty minutes time. All of these things that we do to be aware of the twenty minutes are related to spatial distance, not pure time. That is, they all involve going from point "A" to point "B." When we picture the twenty minutes on the clock, we see the distance from the twelve to the four. When we visualize the different things we can do for the twenty minutes, they all involve our envisioning movement from one space to another space. Even when we sit in one spot and occasionally look at our watch to keep track of the twenty minutes, we're still perceiving a spatial distance as we watch the minute hand move from one point to the next or, in the case of a digital watch, we observe the LED display move a spatial distance from ":00" to ":20."

We convert objective time, which doesn't exist for us since we can't perceive or conceive it, to spatial distance, which we can perceive and conceive. If someone said that JFK died in 1963, this would be a statement involving objective time. We would most likely perceive the content of the statement by associating it with where we were or what we were doing on the day he died, which involves recalling a memory of a spatial configuration. People who were not alive during 1963 would simply recall a memory about the event from something they read or heard previously and associate the date with the past as a spatial distance from where they are now back to 1963. We would not be able to associate any memories of pure objective time with this date, since it would be impossible for us to have any. We can only associate memories of spatial measurements of objective time with this date.

You might wonder what the purpose is for defining objective time if it doesn't exist for us. The reason is because it truly is a representation of time, it's just not a time that we can perceive or conceive. It works fine for solving math problems though, because math, as was stated in a previous chapter, doesn't necessarily correspond to what we perceive as reality. Correct solutions to math problems can be obtained using terms that we can't perceive or conceive, such as imaginary numbers, six or seven extra dimensions, and infinities. But in order for us to deal with objective time, even though it doesn't exist for us because we can't perceive or conceive it, we change it to something that does exist for us – spatial distance.

When we discuss relativity in the next chapter, we will discover that objective time (perceived by us as "spatial" time) is also relative to the frame of reference of the person who's measuring it. For instance, for two clocks, "A" and "B," moving in different frames of reference, as clock A moves faster and faster, relative to clock B, clock B will measure the objective time elapsing for the occurrence of an event in clock A's frame of reference as less and less until finally, when clock A is traveling at the speed of light relative to clock B, clock B will measure the objective time elapsing in clock A's frame of reference as zero, meaning that no time is passing at all for clock A, from clock B's point of view. However, clock A's measurement of the same event in its own frame of reference would be what it normally would be if clock A were at rest. In other words, two people, one moving relative to the other, will measure different spatial objective times for the occurrence of the same event. (This is because of the finite amount of time it takes for the information about the recorded time on one clock to travel to an observer who is moving in the frame of reference of the second clock. This will be dealt with more in the next chapter on relativity.)

Subjective time is a completely different story than objective time. We *do* have a concept of subjective time. It "flows" along a time line that we can be aware of as that time is moving. As its name implies, it is completely dependent on the person (subject) who conceives it. Its length, or speed of movement, varies according to how it is compared to the unique memories stored in the brain of the person evaluating it. Its flow also depends on the person's perception of the event that is being evaluated for its time flow. For instance, suppose two people happen to be walking through a park and they hear a band playing music there. They walk over and listen to the band play for a period of time, then move on. One of the two people did not care for the type music the band was playing, while the other person really enjoyed the music. When the two people discuss the music several hours later, the one who didn't like the music complains that they wasted two hours standing there listening to it. The one who enjoyed the music disagrees and says they couldn't have been there for more than an hour. Since neither of them had a watch, and they came in the middle of the performance, we'll assume there's no way for them to calculate the measured (objective) time that they spent listening to the music. So who's correct? Did they spend an hour listening to the music or two hours listening to it? Both people have a concept of the amount of time the music lasted. They each perceived the music, and then they each compared those perceptions to previously stored memories of that type of music in their brain. This caused a thought process, or conception, to determine how long the music lasted, and for each of them, this process produced a different result. The answer is that they are both correct. Subjective time is completely dependent on the person who conceives it. Of course, if there is a way to compare this conceived time to the calculated objective time, then an actual measurement of the time the music lasted can be verified sometime later, after they left the concert. If the person who felt that the concert lasted two hours was told that the measured time for it was actually only one hour, he might say, "Okay, but it felt like two hours." The measured time of one hour means nothing to him, other than a mathematical calculation of a spatial distance, because as far as the actual concept of time pertains to him in this matter, the conception was of a two-hour concert. That is, his brain was aware of a flow of time of two hours, and just saying that the measured time was one hour won't change that conception of two hours because his conception of the amount of time that passed while he was perceiving the music was already formed and had already affected the stored memory of the perception of the music. However, his hearing that the concert really only lasted one hour can now be stored in his brain as an auditory language perception for future comparison so that the next time he hears music he doesn't like, he can recall this auditory language perception from his stored memories to use for comparison to the perceptions of the new music and predict that even though he feels like the new music is lasting two hours, it probably is really only lasting one hour because the last time he thought music he didn't like lasted two hours, he was off by an hour. In other words, he now has another memory to call upon when he's evaluating how long the music seems to be lasting, and each new memory he can store in his brain to influence his final evaluation of how long the music lasted will help him in making a more accurate response if someone asks him, "How long did you listen to the music?" Also remember that this new perception he made a memory of is not a pure time perception, it is a spatial distance perception of the measured time of the previous concert. If, for example, he had a wristwatch on so that he could measure the time of the concert as he listened to it, he could continually add the visual perceptions of the spatial position of the hands on the wristwatch to the memories he is using to conceive how long the concert is lasting. These visual perceptions of the movement of the hands on the clock would certainly modify his final determination of how long the concert lasted. Keep in mind, however, that these are visual perceptions of the hands on the wristwatch, not perceptions or conceptions of flowing time. They can be used as visual perceptions to modify his final evaluation of how long the concert lasted, but they are not conceptions of flowing time. If someone listens to a concert that is measured at one hour long, and he also has a conception that it lasted one hour, that conception still has nothing to do with the fact that the measured time was also one hour because measured time (objective time) and conceived time (subjective time) are completely different things, as far as our brains are concerned, even though they both have the same term, "time", in them. One is just a measurement that is not perceived nor conceived, and the other is a subjective flow of time that can be conceived as it is occurring. If you keep in mind that measurements of objective time aren't associated with a feeling of time moving, while conceptions of subjective time are associated with a feeling of time moving, then this might be easier to understand.

What is it that makes our concept of the flow of time longer for unpleasant perceptions and shorter for pleasant perceptions? Or, while perceiving the same event, why does each one of us usually have a different concept of how long it lasted? The reason is because our brain has evolved to form stronger memories of negative perceptions than of positive perceptions. A negative perception is one that is either unpleasant or may possibly cause harm to us. A positive perception is one that is pleasant or may benefit us in some way. It is much more important to remember something that can affect us in a negative way than to remember something that affects us in a positive way because it is the negative experiences we perceive that have the potential to cause our demise, not the positive experiences. In order to remember the negative perceptions better, the various receptors for our five senses are more easily triggered by negative experiences than by positive experiences. For instance, if a person is receiving a soothing back massage, the pressure receptors sending signals to the brain may fire a couple times per second. But if that same person is receiving painful stimulation in the same area of his back, the sensory receptors for pain will fire signals to the brain at a much higher rate of fifty or a hundred per second, which will demand more attention from the brain to resolve the problem. Each time a sensory receptor is triggered and sends an impulse to the brain, the brain performs its usual function of comparing the incoming perception to its memories of similar experiences in order to effect the most appropriate response. If the brain is receiving fifty signals per second from a negative perception, as opposed to two signals per second from a positive perception, it will have to perform this comparison-to-previous-memories routine twenty-five times as often per second for a negative perception as for a positive perception. Each time the brain receives an incoming electric signal from a perception, it also becomes aware of a flow of time because each new electric signal evaluated is conceived with a sequential unit of time flow. In this way, the brain is aware of a little more time passing as each signal is received. For the negative perception that sends fifty signals per second to the brain, the brain will become aware of the passing of time fifty times per second, as opposed to becoming aware of the passing of time two times per second with a positive perception. Since the brain can only respond to what it receives, in this example it will "feel" like twenty-five times more time has passed during the negative perception than during the positive perception. When you think of each signal sent from a sensory receptor to the brain being equivalent to one unit of conceived flow of time by the brain, it is easy to see that a perception that triggers more sensory receptors to send electric signals to the brain will be conceived as more flow of time by the brain. So the result is that the increased numbers of negative perceptions feel like they last a lot longer than the fewer positive perceptions because more negative perceptions trigger more concepts of time passing, and the more concepts there are of time passing, the longer the total time will seem.

When a negative perception triggers a sensory receptor to send an electrical signal to the brain, it is more likely to cause the brain to stop what it's doing and focus all its attention on that incoming negative perception so that it can form a response more quickly to resolve whatever is being perceived as potentially harmful. This is because the memories for negative perceptions are made much stronger in the brain so that they can be recalled for comparison to new perceptions and responded to much more quickly. More electrical current is diverted from other areas of the brain in order to locate and recall these memories into awareness faster. This is why a negative perception causes a person to focus more attention on it than he would on a positive perception. For instance, using our previous example of the back massage, while receiving a soothing back massage, most people will daydream about many different things while perceiving the massage, and will not focus too much attention on the massage itself. However, if a painful area is encountered suddenly by the person giving the massage, the daydreaming stops and all attention is focused on doing something to stop the pain because the negative perceptions trigger much more attention and a stronger, faster response.

You may wonder how the sensory receptors can know whether a perception is negative or positive so that they can fire more signals to the brain for negative perceptions. After all, it's the brain that determines whether a perception is negative or positive when it compares the incoming signals to memories of previous similar perceptions, not the receptors themselves. The receptors themselves have no way of determining what's negative and what's positive. The reason that negative perceptions cause increased numbers of signals to be sent to the brain is because negative perceptions are usually those that trigger sensory pain receptors, and pain receptors, by their very nature, send a larger number of signals to the brain from a given stimulus than other types of sensory receptors. Even the person who was not enjoying the music concert in our previous example was receiving some negative signals in his brain via pain receptors in his hearing mechanism, which is why his concept of the time that passed while he was listening to the concert was longer than the person's concept of time who enjoyed the concert. The person who enjoyed the concert received no pain signals from his hearing mechanism because he perceived only pleasant sounds from the music.

Experiments have been performed using transcranial magnetic stimulation (TMS) to show how a person's concept of time flow can be altered by artificial means. A TMS machine is similar to an eggbeater in shape and size. It is used to stimulate the wires in the brain to fire electrical signals by holding the TMS unit against the scalp. The part of the brain immediately beneath where the TMS unit is held on the scalp is where the stimulus reaches. When the brain was overstimulated in various areas with the TMS unit, an underestimation of the passing of time in working memory resulted. In other words, they overstimulated the memory areas of the brain, exhausting them so that the memories located in that area couldn't be recalled normally, then saw that if new perceptions were experienced by the

patients, they estimated the flow of time during those perceptions at less than they would have with intact memory systems.
In effect, what this experiment did was to keep the brain from
comparing all the incoming perceptions to stored memories of
similar perceptions. Since fewer perceptions could be analyzed,
fewer units of time flow were conceived, and the patient's conception of the amount of time that passed was judged to be less
than what actually occurred.

What is it that allows for our conception of a sequential flow
of time, rather than a jerky, haphazard, or out-of-sequence flow
of time when the brain receives perceptions and then compares
them with memories of previous similar perceptions to effect a
response? The answer is that when perceptions are stored in the
brain as memories, they are stored in the same time order as
they were received and evaluated by the brain, which means
that when they are recalled for comparison to new perceptions,
they are recalled in the correct order according to their time
line. This means that the time line is preserved just the way the
event that was perceived occurred.

The concept of movement may seem like something that
would be hard for the brain to sort out. After all, a perception is
a singular event that triggers a receptor for one of our five
senses to send a single signal to the brain for evaluation. Then,
as soon as something moves, another perception can trigger another receptor, and so on. For instance, let's suppose you're
watching a car go down the road. As the car moves along, light
is reflected off it and into the back of your eyes, where it triggers a light receptor to fire an electric signal to the brain, which
the brain then evaluates. As the car moves, it continues to reflect light off it at different angles towards your eyes because of

its new position. You keep receiving reflected light waves from the moving car into your eyes, and each time a new light wave triggers a receptor in the back of your eyes, another electric signal is sent to the brain for evaluation. It would seem that there should be no concept of movement of the car recorded in these perceptions, since each perception of a light wave interacting with the receptors in your eyes is of a single event, like taking a picture of the car with a camera. The brain should be getting a series of "still" pictures of the moving car that should have no more movement associated with them than if you took several pictures of the car and laid them out on a desk in the sequence that they were taken. If you looked at them lying on the desk, you might notice that in each picture, the car was positioned a little farther along the road when compared to some stationary object in the background in the pictures, but you wouldn't have a sense of the car actually moving, or a sense of "flowing" time. The way the brain handles all these "still" perceptions to provide a concept of flowing time is similar to the way a movie camera works. By receiving the perceptions one after another at a rapid rate, which the brain can easily do, we aren't aware of the gaps between them. What we conceive is smooth movement along a time line, just as we see when the thousands of still pictures that make up the roll of film in a movie are run rapidly through a projector. The flow of time, or the concept of movement, is nothing more than receiving sequential perceptions in the brain one after another at a high rate of speed. And since perceptions are stored in sequential order, it's easy to recall them in the correct time sequence for comparison to the new perceptions being rapidly received in the brain so that an appropriate response can be made.

The flow of time is subjective, meaning that it is conceived differently by each individual. There is no universal standard flow of time for a given perception. It is determined by the type and number of memories that are recruited in the brain when new perceptions arrive there for comparison, and it is determined by the number of receptors that are triggered in different people by the same perception. Since all the memories for each person differ in type and number for any given perception, there's little chance that any two of us will have the same concept of the amount of time that passed during a particular perception.

What happens to the flow of time when we're daydreaming, or thinking about some problem? In other words, what happens to the flow of time when we are not consciously receiving any sensory perceptions? The answer is that we become less aware of the flow of time because active sensory perceptions are ultimately what trigger a conceptive awareness of the flow of time. If it were possible to eliminate all active sensory input so that all brain activity was by thought processes only, there would be no concept of a flow of time. The concept of time moving, or a flow of time, only occurs when new perceptions reach sensory receptors in a sequential pattern, and trigger them to send electric impulses to the brain to be compared with memories of previous similar perceptions. It is the arrival of the sequential perceptions into the brain that allows us to conceive that time is flowing. If no perception occurs, no concept of a flow of time can result. This is why we seem to "lose track of time" when we're daydreaming or concentrating on some problem that may be bothering us. The more we concentrate by using pure thought process and tuning out sensory stimuli, the less aware of flowing time we become.

For the subjective flow of time to occur, we have to be able to receive new perceptions into the brain for active evaluation and comparison to previous similar memories. This means that we have to be awake and conscious, since our brain can't actively evaluate new perceptions if it's not aware of them. Therefore, there is no flow of time conceived by the brain during sleeping, dreaming, or any other state that renders us unconscious.

To summarize, objective time is a measurement of spatial distance, as far as our brain is capable of dealing with it. True objective time can only be dealt with as math or physics calculations, since they don't necessarily deal in the same reality that we are bound to with our five senses. Subjective time deals with the concept of the flow of time, which is different for each individual. The subjective flow of time only exists in the present, because it requires perceptions that are actively being evaluated by the brain in order to be conceived.

The Past

Those who can't remember the past are condemned to repeat it. This is one of those pearls of wisdom that has been handed down from generation to generation for many years. What is it that we actually recall when we think about the past, and how do we know when the past event we are recalling actually occurred?

In order to think about the past, we must activate memories of previous perceptions that were received in the brain and stored. That is the only possible way we can become aware of something from the past. Since the past has something to do with time, then any memories we recall when thinking about the past must also include a memory that has something to do with time. Any memories that have a time component must either be objective time memories or subjective time memories. Since subjective time only occurs when perceptions are actively being received in the brain, then subjective time can't possibly be involved with recalling past events. This means that recalling the past has to involve objective time. As you may recall, objective time is perceived as spatial distance by the brain rather than as a pure time component because pure objective time doesn't exist for us. So when we recall something that happened in the past, a spatial distance memory of objective time must also be recalled with the memory of the event we are recalling in order to be aware that the memory of that event happened at a specific time in the past. Otherwise, when we recall the event, there's no way we would know whether it occurred ten minutes ago or ten years ago. For instance, if someone mentioned to you that the two of you attended a certain baseball game twenty years ago, in order to put the time frame of when the game occurred into perspective, you might first subtract those twenty years from the current year to calculate the space of time that has passed. Then you might try to associate that specific year in the past with something noteworthy that occurred that year for you – something that is likely to put the spatial distance from now back to then into better perspective. In this way, you can better conceive of the proper time frame of when the baseball game you are recalling actually occurred. That is, if you activate enough past memories of spatial distances of events that occurred around the time of the game in question, you will be more likely to conceive that you are remembering back to the correct time period when the event occurred which, in this case, is "remembering the past." All of this is done using objective time, which involves memories of the measurements of spatial distances of time periods.

The Future

Thinking about the future is very similar to thinking about the past. That is, the same mechanism of associating memories of the spatial distance of objective time with memories of events must be used in order to determine how far into the future the memories of events we are recalling may happen to be. The obvious difference between recalling future events and recalling past events is that any memories of future events must be the result of conceptions rather than perceptions, since there is no way we could have perceived something that hasn't occurred yet. For instance, using the baseball game example, let's suppose your friend asked you to go to a baseball game in two months. You may recall a memory of a past baseball game you attended, then conceive from that past memory what the future game will be like, including all the usual sights, sounds, and smells associated with the baseball game. Your brain will also activate the appropriate objective spatial distance time memories to become aware of how far into the future two months is, otherwise you wouldn't know whether two months felt like two minutes or two years. You might look at your calendar and count up the weeks, or you might be aware that it is now nearing the end of spring and the game will be in the middle of summer. It is also possible that you've scheduled enough events to occur two months in the future over the years that when someone mentions a time frame of two months, you will immediately be able to recall an objective time memory to make you aware of the spatial distance associated with this time frame. As with past time, unless your brain associates the spatial distance of objective time to the memory of the event to come, there is no way to conceive how far into the future two months might be.

The Present

Events that happen in the present do not involve objective time. They can only involve subjective time because they consist of perceptions that are actively being received in the brain, and these are associated with an active flow of time, not a spatial time distance.

The present is an extremely short time period because it only exists while a sequence of perceptions is being evaluated in the brain. As soon as one very short sequence is dealt with, and the next sequence arrives, the first one is no longer part of the flow of time. It is either immediately forgotten if it's not important, or it is made into a permanent memory in the brain to be recalled for comparison to similar perceptions in the future if it is felt to be important enough.

How long or how short would a sequence of incoming perceptions have to be in order to constitute "the present" before it becomes "the past?" The most logical answer to this question would be that the present should constitute a single electrical signal entering the brain from a receptor, since this is the smallest unit that can be evaluated by the brain at one time to allow a conception of something that is occurring "right now." In this case, the most logical answer is the correct answer. Each perception entering the brain becomes "the present" as soon as the brain begins to evaluate it. It becomes "the past" as soon as the brain stops evaluating it and starts evaluating the next perception coming in. In the case where a pain receptor is sending fifty signals per second to the brain, for example, the present is only one-fiftieth of a second. In cases where the brain is evaluating more than one source of incoming perceptions at one time, and one source is sending signals faster than the other, the present is a shorter period of time for the signals that are being received at a faster rate because the brain has to process these faster signals at a higher rate of speed. In this case, there are more than one "present" time. For instance, if I'm listening to the television while eating a sandwich, and the auditory signals from my hearing apparatus are being sent to my brain at twice the frequency as the taste receptors on my tongue are sending signals to my brain, the present will last twice as long for tasting my food than for what I'm listening to on the television. It might seem like this could create some confusion for the brain in determining a subjective time flow for what's happening now and what happened in the past. Fortunately, the time differences involved here are so small that we aren't able to conceive any difference, and there is no conflict with our conception of the flow of time from multiple sources of perceptions at the same time.

TIME AND MOTION

The association of time with motion seems to present a real problem for many people. I have read that being at rest is equivalent to moving in time but not in space, or that time doesn't move, but we do. I've also read that we move through time at the speed of light, and that photons are zero-time particles because they are moving at the speed of light, and that they spend no time in our universe or anywhere else since, for anything moving at the speed of light, no time passes. The reason all these statements are misleading and confusing is because they don't place the whole concept of time where it is actually located – in the human brain. We don't move through time and time doesn't move past us. Time is not a "thing" that moves or that we move through, it is simply a concept that exists for us because our brain requires it in order to survive, as explained earlier. It doesn't matter if we're moving at the speed of light or if photons are zero-time particles for us. The problem here is the failure to realize that the only frame of reference that matters for us is the one each of us is in, not the one that a photon resides in, nor the one anything else resides in. When we move into a different frame of reference, then that one becomes the only one that matters to our brain. For instance, if I'm standing on the ground watching a car go by, my brain is tuned into what is happening in my frame of reference, which is standing still on the earth. If I were in the car, my brain would be tuned in to the car's frame of reference, which is moving at fifty miles per hour along the road, relative to the earth. While in the car, my brain deals with perceptions that are received by someone who is traveling at fifty miles per hour with respect to the earth. What's happening in the earth's frame of reference doesn't matter to my brain at that time, because that's not the reference frame in which it is receiving perceptions.

Time and Acceleration

Objective time changes with acceleration. The more an object accelerates, the less objective time passes, and the closer an accelerating object approaches the speed of light, the farther it goes into the future of an object that is moving at a constant speed with respect to it. What this says is that when an object accelerates, it leaves the "present" of the frame of reference it's in and goes into the future of that frame of reference. For instance, if I stayed on earth and you took off in a rocket and quickly accelerated to a speed of ninety-nine percent of the speed of light, objective time would pass about seven times faster for me back on the earth than for you up in the rocket. If you traveled at that speed for a year and then came back to earth, a clock on your rocket would show that one year had passed, while a clock that remained with me on earth would show that about seven years had passed. In fact, I would look seven years older to you, while you would only look one year older to me. In spite of how strange this may sound, it has actually been shown to be the case, proven many times by various physics experiments involving very small particles that do travel at near light speeds and can be monitored to determine how much time has passed for them, relative to us. The change in the time of one year versus seven years that would pass for you and for me would be real and permanent. There would be no way for you to get back the extra six years of earth time that were lost by your traveling away from the earth at near light speed for a year. When you accelerated away from the earth, you actually went into the future of the frame of reference of people who remained on the earth.

This same phenomenon that affects objective time with acceleration also applies to gravity, because gravity is a form of acceleration. In a gravitational field, the closer an object is to the center of the gravitational field, the more it is affected by gravity, which means the measurement of objective time for the occurrence of an event will be shorter too, the nearer it is to the center of gravity. For instance, objective time on the surface of the earth for an event is measured at less than objective time for satellites orbiting the earth, a fact that requires re-synchronizing the clocks on our telecommunication satellites on a regular basis. Fortunately for our peace of mind, all the acceleration that takes place in our usual frame of reference on the surface of the earth is so small, compared to the speed of light, that we usually aren't even aware of any objective time changes with acceleration. For instance, when accelerating from a stop in your car to sixty miles per hour, the decrease in objective time during this acceleration is so tiny that it would be very difficult to even measure.

Someone may wonder if decelerating might cause a person to go back into the past, since accelerating causes one to go into the future. The answer is that it would not. Decelerating is just a variation of acceleration and would have the same affect, regarding the original frame of reference. That is, decelerating would still cause one to move into the future of the starting frame of reference.

Why is it that accelerating in a specific frame of reference causes an object to go into the future of that frame of reference? Unfortunately, our measly five senses don't allow us to perceive or conceive why this occurs. But math, which is not limited by the five senses, can very accurately compute that this phenomenon can occur, and physics experiments have proven beyond a shadow of a doubt that it does occur. If only we had that elusive sixth or seventh sense, we might be able to easily understand how it works.

Some physicists have suggested that time travel is not possible because if it were, we should have already been invaded by beings from the future, and since that hasn't occurred, then time travel must be impossible. The problem with this logic is that acceleration will only allow someone to travel into the future, not into the past. This means that any beings from the future could not possibly come back to our frame of reference by accelerating, because they can only time travel into the future, not the past. We have already seen in the chapter on light that the only way to travel into the past would be to somehow go faster than the speed of light to overtake the light from past scenes and observe it by getting in front of it and looking back as it then reached your eyes. However, no object with mass can go faster than the speed of light, and even if it could, it wouldn't actually be going back into the past; it would only be seeing events that happened in the past and could not interact with them.

The famous Heisenberg uncertainty principle, which we've encountered before, says that you can't know the position of a subatomic particle if you know the speed, and you can't know the speed if you know the position. Since subatomic particles are in constantly changing motion, or acceleration, and are moving at near light speeds, they are constantly moving into the future of their frames of reference. It would certainly make sense that since they are constantly moving into future frames of reference, trying to locate them by position and speed in a specific frame of reference, which is what one would have to do to measure the speed and the position, would be impossible.

SUMMARY

In this chapter, we have looked at how the brain deals with time. We've seen that there are two types of time, one that is used as a spatial measuring device, especially for mathematics, and another type that we can conceive and use to give us a feeling of an ordered sequence of events – a flow of time. We have also seen that it is possible to travel into the future by accelerating. This has been proven with physics experiments.

In the next chapter, we will discuss relativity and its interaction with our brain. It should tie in with many of the things we've been discussing about time, light, and physics to give a better overall picture of what goes on in our brain.

WHO ARE WE, REALLY?

RELATIVITY

Einstein was responsible for making "relativity" a household term in the very early 1900s. In fact, it was his theory of relativity that made his name synonymous with extraordinary intelligence. In this chapter we will discuss Einstein's theory of relativity, and then we will see how relativity also applies to our everyday existence because of the way our brain deals with it.

Relativity does not only apply to math and physics. Everything is relative to everything else. This is because everyone's brain functions relative to everyone else's brain. What you perceive is not the exact same thing that I perceive, even though we may be experiencing the same perception. When the perception we're both experiencing triggers the same sensory receptors in each of our bodies, and an electric impulse representing that perception then travels to each of our brains to be compared to memories of previous perceptions that are similar, your memories of previous similar perceptions will be different than mine, so your brain's evaluation of the incoming perception, along with your subsequent response, will be at least somewhat different than mine. For instance, suppose we both go to lunch and order a salad. When the salads come, they have cucumbers in them. You are happy about this because you really like cucumbers, while I painstakingly remove all the cucumbers from my salad because I really dislike them. Why does each one of us have a different response to the perception of seeing cucumbers on our salads? The reason is because when we saw the cucumbers on the salads, that perception for you may have been compared to a memory of your eating cucumbers previously and enjoying the taste of them, while for me, the perception of seeing the cucumbers on my salad may have been compared to a past memory of my getting very sick after eating cucumbers. We both had different responses to the visual perception of seeing the cucumbers on our salads because new perceptions are compared to what's stored as memories in each of our individual brains, and those stored memories are different for each one of us.

EINSTEIN'S THEORY OF RELATIVITY

Einstein developed two theories of relativity. The first, called the "special theory of relativity," was presented in 1905. Later he added to the special theory of relativity to come up with the "general theory of relativity." This took him another ten or twelve years to work out.

Special Theory of Relativity

The special theory of relativity deals with objects moving at uniform speeds in different frames of reference. The fact that the theory dealt only with objects moving in their various frames of reference at unchanging speeds is what caused the attachment of the term "special" to this theory.

Einstein noticed that the equations describing certain phenomena were different when observed by someone who was moving relative to the phenomena than by someone who observed the phenomena while at rest, relative to the phenomena. More specifically, he noticed that the equations that described the force between a moving electrically charged particle and a wire carrying an electric current were different from the point of view of moving along with the particle versus sitting at rest and watching it go by. For someone watching it go by, the force on the particle was completely due to the magnetic field of the wire, but for the person moving along in the same frame of reference as the particle itself, the force was completely due to the electrical charge in the wire. Einstein knew that this couldn't be. That is, the force had to be the same regardless of whether the person measuring it was moving with it or not moving with it. His relativity theory changed the equations used to compute the force so that both the moving and the stationary observer measured the same force. In order for this to work, he had to assume that the speed of electromagnetic waves (which includes light waves) was the same for all observers, regardless of whether they were moving relative to an event or not. As explained in a previous chapter, the reason the speed of light is the same for all observers, whether they are moving relative to the light wave or not, is because light waves, as well as any other type of electromagnetic waves, are self-propagating, which means they not only don't need a medium to carry them along, but because they are self-propagating, their origin doesn't matter either, once they start, because they begin anew in each frame of reference they enter.

The special theory of relativity also predicted that nothing could go faster than the speed of light. As mentioned in the chapter on light, it wasn't so much that nothing could go faster than the speed of light that was so important, but that no information could be transmitted faster than the speed of light. The reason for this depends entirely on our ability to perceive information through our five senses. The fastest means of triggering any of our sensory receptors is via electromagnetic waves, all of which travel at the speed of light. Since information can't be received unless it is we who are receiving it, then it's logical to assume that no information can be transmitted faster than the speed of light. We'll get back to this shortly after explaining some of the strange things that occur because of the special theory of relativity.

If you're sitting out in space and someone passes you in a spaceship that is moving at a very high rate of speed, say sixty percent of the speed of light, when you look at the spaceship, its length will appear to be less to you than to the person who is inside the spaceship. Also, if there happens to be a clock sitting in the spaceship that you can see as it's passing, you will notice that the clock runs slower than a clock in your frame of reference. The reason the moving spaceship looks shorter and the moving clock runs slower is because of the finite length of time it takes for information about the spaceship and what's going on with it to reach you. That is, when you look at the front of the spaceship, what you're seeing is light waves reflected off it and then towards your eyes at 186,000 miles per second, which is the speed of light. Then, because the spaceship is moving so fast, by the time the reflected light leaves the rear of the spaceship on its journey to your eyes, the spaceship has already moved forward an appreciable amount. So when you look at the front of the spaceship, then look at the rear, in the time it takes you to move your eyes from the front to the rear, the spaceship has moved an appreciable distance and the light now being reflected towards your eyes from the rear of the spaceship will show where the rear of the spaceship is when the light was reflected from the rear, not from where the spaceship was when you were looking at the light reflected towards your eyes from the front of the spaceship. By the time you look at the rear of the spaceship, the front has moved forward too, but you aren't aware of it, because by the time the light that was reflected off the front is just reaching your eyes, the front of the spaceship is no longer where your eyes see it. All of this occurs because when you look at the spaceship, information your eyes gather as light waves is not obtained instantaneously, but at the speed of light. The clock on the spaceship appears to run slower too for the same reason. When you first look at the time on the clock, and then look at it one minute later by your clock, what you will see on the spaceship clock is less than one minute passing because when you look at the spaceship clock immediately after one minute on your clock, you're seeing the light reflected from the spaceship clock that left that clock in the past in order to reach your eyes at just that moment, and the time on the clock from the past will show less than one minute has elapsed. To the person traveling on the spaceship at a constant speed past you, it will appear to him that you are moving past him in the opposite direction at sixty percent the speed of light, and your clock will appear to him to be running slower than his. You will also appear to be thinner to him too, for the same reasons as stated above. While motion makes lengths shrink, it makes time intervals lengthen. The two effects are matched so that the amount by which a moving object shrinks is exactly balanced by the amount the time lengthens when it is perceived by someone in a different frame of reference. In our daily lives, we don't ordinarily deal with speeds of objects anywhere near the speed of light, so we can usually treat light waves as if they are essentially instantaneous. But for extremely fast-moving objects, or when looking at objects that are extremely far away, like other planets and stars, the speed at which information travels must be taken into effect.

The special theory of relativity showed that space and time have no absolute meaning and are nothing but systems of relations depending on what is moving relative to something else. What this means is that everything is relative to the frame of reference where one happens to be.

What would happen to special relativity if there were only one particle in the entire universe? The answer is that uniform motion could not exist and special relativity would be meaningless. Uniform motion, which is motion that does not change via acceleration or gravity, could never be verified because there would be nothing to use as a reference point. To take this one step further, suppose you were the only person on the earth. Would you have any relative memories? In order for your memories to be relative, they'd have to be compared to someone else's, so the answer would be that you would not have any relative memories. All your memories would be absolute, meaning that whatever was real for you would be universally real. And whatever you thought was good or bad would be universally good or bad. There would be no opinions. Whatever you perceived would be indisputable. (We will discuss this in more detail in Part II.)

General Theory of Relativity

Einstein realized that his special theory of relativity could not be the final answer to the question about relativity because it only dealt with speeds that were unchanging when comparing one frame of reference to another. He knew that he would need to develop his theory further to account for the changing speeds of gravity and acceleration in different frames of reference. He discovered that you couldn't tell the difference between gravity and acceleration without a point of reference. In other words, if you were sitting in an airplane with a blindfold on so that you couldn't see anything, and the airplane took off at an acceleration rate of 32 feet per second per second, this would feel no different to you than if you were blindfolded and strapped into a free-fall ride in an amusement park, where the acceleration downward is due to gravity, which also has an acceleration rate of 32 feet per second per second. This showed that non-uniform motion, or changing motion, is relative to your frame of reference too, just as with constant motion.

There were some problems with gravity that caused Einstein to consider it a warping of space rather than a force. His biggest problem with letting gravity be a force was that he felt that when someone was in free-fall in a gravitational field, he would not feel any different than someone who was sitting in space without any forces acting on him. He reasoned that because the person in free-fall in a gravitational field wouldn't feel the force of gravity like someone who was standing on the earth would, these two different frames of reference would produce different measured forces for gravity. Since he had already shown in his theory of relativity that the laws of physics are the same in all

177

uniformly moving reference frames, the fact that a person standing on earth would feel the force of gravity while someone who was in free-fall in a gravitational field wouldn't feel it meant that gravity could not be a real force. His thinking was that if something was present in one frame of reference but was not present in another frame of reference, then that something couldn't be real. Einstein then went on to show mathematically that any matter or energy in the universe warps space and time and it is the greater warping of space near a larger mass like the earth that is responsible for what we feel as the "pull" of gravity. He declared that gravity is not a force but this warping of space. As was mentioned in a previous chapter, a problem with the example he used is that a person sitting in space with no forces acting on him would *not* feel the same as someone who was in free-fall in a gravitational field. Since gravity accelerates a person at a rate of 32 feet per second per second, if there were no wind resistance, which would be the case if the free-fall took place above our atmosphere, the person in free-fall in a gravitational field would definitely perceive something that the person sitting in space without any forces acting on him would not feel. Our bodies have touch receptors that are activated by acceleration, or a change in speed, and since gravity is acceleration, which is a continuous change in speed, we would perceive the acceleration of gravity continuously while in free-fall that we would not perceive while sitting in space without any forces acting on us. Free-fall in a gravitational field would be perceived similar to what you feel when an elevator first starts going down, before it reaches a constant speed. So free-fall in a gravitational field is not the same as sitting in space with no forces acting on us. Although math equations can be used to predict the effects of gravity on the warping of space, we must remember that math does not always deal with what we perceive as reality. In the end, it's what happens in each our brains that is all that matters.

Until the theory of relativity came along, space and time were considered to be fixed backgrounds upon which events occurred, but relativity showed that there is no fixed background where things take place. There is only a system of relationships, each of which takes place on a background of its own making. Relativity theory states that if everything disappeared from the universe, then space and time would also disappear, because they are a part of each frame of reference, not a universal thing that exists independent of frames of reference. We can take this a step further and say that if we human beings disappeared from the universe, space and time would also disappear because space and time, as well as everything else, exist only because we're here to perceive or conceive them. Each of us has a unique frame of reference where everything takes place. That unique frame of reference for each of us is our own personal brain. Nothing can exist in our unique frame of reference unless we perceive or conceive it.

RELATIVITY AND THE BRAIN

Since our own individual brain is the frame of reference that each of us is bound to, everything that we perceive and conceive is relative to our own brain. Whether our brain is diseased, under the influence of a chemical such as a medication or toxin, or is functioning normally, it will always be the frame of reference upon which our entire existence centers. Because each of our brains is unique, there will be no other person whose frame of reference is identical to ours. This has important implications, as we shall see.

Einstein overthrew two of the absolutes of nineteenth century science. One was absolute rest, which was represented by what was termed "ether," the medium through which electromagnetic waves were thought to be carried, but shown by Einstein not to exist. The other was absolute time that all clocks were thought to measure. Einstein showed that time was also relative to the frame of reference one happened to be in and was not the same for all frames of reference. Many people found the loss of these absolutes to be an unsettling concept. They wondered if it implied that everything was relative and whether there were any absolute standards at all, such as an absolute moral standard, for example. The answer is that morality is a product of society, and although an absolute moral standard does not exist, each society has a standard set of rules that determine what is moral and what is immoral within that society. Einstein's relativity does not negate the moral standards within a society just because each individual within that society has a different frame of reference for determining for himself what he *thinks* is moral or immoral. (This will be explained in detail in the chapter on morals and ethics.)

The concepts "good," "bad," "right," and "wrong" are relative to each person's frame of reference, and are defined based on the memories of perceptions and conceptions each person has stored in his unique brain. For instance, a certain hunter likes to go out on the weekend and shoot wild rabbits for sport. He feels that he is doing a good thing because it thins out their numbers so that they are less likely to starve or spread diseases to one another. A non-hunter feels that hunting rabbits for sport is a bad thing because it destroys life for no purpose. Each of these two people has a different set of memories of previous perceptions and conceptions justifying his individual position on this matter, based on his personal frame of reference. It would be impossible to say absolutely that one person is wrong and the other person is right. If you asked another hunter to decide who's right, he would be more likely to side with the hunter, while a non-hunter would be more likely to side with the non-hunter. If one person were able to convince the other person why his thinking is correct in this matter, then the person who had been convinced would form new memories in his brain that would allow him to feel the same way about shooting rabbits for sport as the other person feels about it. His frame of reference would have changed so that it was more aligned with the other person's frame of reference on this particular matter. This is why we argue and debate different positions on various points – to try to move others closer to our frame of reference. If another person's memories are not as strongly formed as ours on a certain matter, we may be more likely to cause him to modify his memories on that matter to more closely resemble ours. But if his memories are more strongly formed than ours for that particular matter, he will be more likely to cause us to modify our memories to more closely resemble his on that subject.

Success and power are also relative. An average citizen may think that a senator is a very powerful person, but the senator thinks that he is not very powerful because he is not the president. In the average citizen's frame of reference, a senator has a lot of power. In the senator's frame of reference, the president is the powerful person, not the senator. Who is right?

The answer is that both are right when one looks at the situation from each person's frame of reference.

One of the peculiar things about each of us having a different frame of reference is that we can have different perceptions of the same event. For instance, suppose you and I decide to play a tennis match. You win the match and are very happy that you were victorious, because winning the match is what you conceived was the most important thing about this event for you. I am also happy after the match, even though I lost, because I got a lot of well-needed exercise, which is what I conceived was the most important thing about the match. We each looked at the tennis match from a different frame of reference, and even though the outcome of the match was different for each of us, we both achieved the goal that was most important for us in our individual frame of reference. In your brain, previous memories of perceptions of playing tennis dictated that the best response to the perception of playing tennis would be to win the match. In my brain, previous memories of perceptions of playing tennis dictated that the best response to the perception of playing tennis would be to run around as much as I could in order to get a lot of exercise. Why is our individual motivation for playing tennis so different? In other words, why does each one of us have such different memories of previous perceptions in our brains about playing tennis that our individual responses to this match are so different? Since our memories are made up from everything we've experienced during our lifetimes, and then they dictate, based on previous perceptions, what type of a response we will make to future perceptions, there's very little chance that we would both have the same motivation for playing this tennis match. For instance, I may have been told recently that my cholesterol is too high and that if I don't exercise more, I'm going to have a heart attack. You may have been passed over recently for a big job promotion that you had been competing for at work, and needed to win our tennis match to regain your confidence.

Another interesting phenomenon about relativity is that the same event can be perceived differently by the same person in different situations. In other words, the same person can perceive the same event differently if the event's frame of reference changes. For instance, Ann is a college student who plays on the women's varsity basketball team. She is also a gymnast. At five and a half feet tall, when she competes in gymnastics, the people in the audience remark to each other that Ann is a very tall gymnast. When Ann is playing basketball with her team, the people in the audience remark to each other that she is a very short basketball player. So is she tall or short? The answer is that it depends on the frame of reference Ann is in when her relative height is being perceived. As Einstein proclaimed, and as we can see here, nothing is absolute. Everything is relative to everything else – except the speed of light, of course, which is the same in all frames of reference because it originates anew in each frame of reference, as explained previously.

In the chapter on language, we asked, "When does life begin?" The answer given was that the limiting factor in defining this concept is the meanings we attach to the words we use in our language, not an actual, perceivable change from non-life to life. We can now explain this further by stating that the meanings each of us attaches to the words we use are not identical to every other person's meanings for the same words. They are relative to our individual frame of reference and are the products of memories of perceptions we have formed from previous experiences that make each word mean something at least slightly different for us than what it might mean for someone else, based on whatever perceptions we experienced at the same time as when we perceived some particular word or sentence. For instance, a person with religious convictions might say that a human life begins when God puts a soul into a person, because the memories of perceptions he has stored in his brain reflect what he was taught in his religious education. Someone with little or no religious background would certainly disagree and say that a human life begins at some other point in development, because he would have no memories of perceptions that had anything to do with religious training. Since each person has a different frame of reference, based on all his memories of previous perceptions, it can be seen that the question, "When does life begin?" can never have an absolute answer. The answer is relative to the frame of reference being used.

SUMMARY

We have reviewed Einstein's theory of relativity as a basis for showing that not only physics phenomena depend on a frame of reference, but that everything depends on the frame of reference of the person perceiving or conceiving it, and that no perception or conception is absolute across all frames of reference (except the speed of light). This means that concepts such as "good," "bad," "right," and "wrong" are not absolute, but are all relative to the person who conceives them, and each person's conception of terms like these results from the stored memories of perceptions he has experienced during his lifetime.

PART II

PERCEPTION – REVISITED

Now that we've discussed physics, time, light, relativity, and the unusual phenomena that link these subjects with the higher functioning of our brain, it's time to get back to perception and the somewhat controversial concepts that arise because of our ability to perceive things. We will discuss consciousness, reality, the mind, and many other concepts, in order to understand just what the relationship is between each of them and the brain. The title of this chapter may be misleading because it is more about the conceptions that take place after perceptions are received in the brain than about the perceptions themselves.

THE MIND

For many people, the idea that we are entirely reducible to how our brain functions seems to take away our dignity, or sense of meaning. They would prefer to believe that something mystical takes place within the brain that is beyond what can be determined through experimentation and examination of the brain. For them, we are more than just what's contained in the living wires of our brain. The term "mind" seems to present a more mystical quality to our thinking process than simply referring to that process as an associative brain function. Unfortunately, anyone who separates "mind" from "brain" dooms to failure any theories he may have about either of them. The mind *is* the brain. The reason one cannot separate "mind" from "brain" is because the mind refers to the association activities that take place within the brain. That is, the mind is the part of the brain that allows us to think. When we recall various stored memories in order to come up with some new idea or course of action, that is the mind at work. When new perceptions are experienced, and the information about them travels from the various receptors of our five senses to the brain, and then are analyzed to decide upon a course of action, the part of the brain where all the comparing of memories of old perceptions to new perceptions takes place is what we refer to as the "mind." There are no mystical qualities associated with the mind. It has been studied for years and accurate predictions have now been made about how it functions. Once everyone understands what is currently known about how the mind (or associative brain) works, the philosophical discussions of the mind are reduced to subjects for late night conversation rather than for a useful process of investigation.

The mind constantly seeks change. In fact, if one were to summarize the entire meaning of life, it could be stated in one word – *change*. For the mind, change is in the form of new input. This can either be from new perceptions being received in the brain for evaluation, or it can be from activating old memories already stored in the brain to come up with new concepts, such as when a person is daydreaming or trying to figure out a problem. If change within the mind (or brain) stopped, that would mean there were no active electrical impulses traveling around the brain. If this were the case, a person could not be conscious, nor could there be any way to regain consciousness, since the only way anything happens in the brain is via electric currents that are traveling from one place to another place. If they all stopped, there would be nothing to restart them. As it is, the electric currents are continuously moving around the brain, even while a person is asleep, and when they need to be directed to a particular area where they can activate memories that are needed to recall something, they are directed into the appropriate area either by an incoming perception that needs to be compared to old memories, or by a particular thought that a person is having at that time. Sometimes when the memories that are being sought are difficult to locate, other means of finding them can be used. For instance, you might be trying to remember the name of a person you met five years ago, but you just can't seem to remember it. What your mind does next to help you recall it is to associate other things about your meeting the person five years ago. You might remember something you talked about with him, or what kind of car he was driving. Since perceptions that are received together get stored together, these perceptions would have been stored along with the person's name in your memories that dealt with him, and you now have a few more memories to help direct the random electrical currents to the proper area of the brain to recall his name.

In case you might be wondering how the random electrical currents traveling around the brain could even begin to know how to look for various memories and then activate them once they're located, remember that the mind doesn't just randomly seek out a memory in the brain. It doesn't have that capability because there's no way it would know when it had located the correct memory. All it can do is transmit electrical signals randomly until something directs those signals to specific areas of the brain. With billions of memories in the brain, it would be essentially impossible to happen upon the memory it's searching for by this random method anyway. Something has to occur to trigger a train of thought that causes the electrical current to be directed to a certain area where the memory that's being sought is located. Usually this trigger is a new perception that is received into the brain that then causes the random electrical currents flowing around the brain to try to match up the electrical characteristics of this new perception to memories similar to it to effect a response, since that's what the mind does when it receives new information. During this process, the mind can form concepts based on memories recalled from that particular area of the brain to form new memories and new concepts in a chain reaction type sequence. In other words, just about every memory that you locate in your brain and recall into consciousness is the result of an immediately preceding related event directing electrical impulses into that particular area of the brain. For instance, something may cause you to start thinking about having to drive to the store to get a loaf of bread, which reminds you that your car has been making a funny noise, which reminds you that your husband said he was going to take care of that problem a month ago, which reminds you that he's never been reliable, which reminds you that your mother said you shouldn't have married him in the first place, which reminds you that your favorite aunt never showed up at your wedding, and so on. What's happening here is that one memory is activated by some stimulus, and that memory activates another one in that area of the brain that has at least something associated with the original memory, and the process continues. No conscious thought ever occurs without a previous thought directing electrical impulses towards the memories associated with that thought. In other words, no totally random thoughts ever occur to an awake person. They originate from some new sensory perception that then triggers a chain reaction in the brain to get to the particular memories that are the basis of that thought (or conception). The electrical current is continuously directed in a somewhat orderly fashion. The only time a truly random memory is activated and brought into working memory is when someone is asleep or in some other state of unconsciousness. In these cases the random electrical impulse generator in the brain can activate any memory, or sequence of memories, it happens to come across as it's "roaming" around the brain. These activated memories may later be recalled as dreams.

Sometimes when we can't figure out a solution to a problem, we will look at it in a different way, and then the solution is easily found. The reason this occurs is because when the mind is activating memories for use in seeking the answer to the problem, the memories it is activating may not be capable of causing the correct cross-linking of memories that leads to a concept being formed that can lead to the solution. As soon as the thought process is changed so that the random electrical current in the brain activates a different set of memories, the correct cross-linking is made between those memories and this results in a new memory, or concept, that allows the solution to the problem to arise.

One of the reasons we know that the mind compares new perceptions to similar perceptions already in memory is because brain scans show that when a person is asked to picture something in his mind that he's already familiar with, such as a cow, and is later shown a picture of a cow, the same areas of the brain that lit up when he was asked to picture the cow in his mind light up when he is shown a picture of the cow.

There had long been a controversy about why a person's mind continues to evolve and grow through adulthood into old age, because it was thought that the mind was something that was just "there" and not really associated with growth and development. But now that we know how the processes that take place in the mind occur, it's easy to see that the reason the mind evolves is because the mind is the brain and the brain continues to store new memories and get rid of old memories it no longer needs throughout the entire life of a person. The mind has no choice but to grow and evolve over time.

The mind attempts to not only simplify something to its essentials, but also to see through the essentials to the bigger picture. In other words, it tries to use deductive and inductive logic, respectively. It is no coincidence that logic plays such a big part in determining the correct response to some stimulus, or perception. Every time the mind evaluates something, it must follow this pattern. When a new perception is received, for example, and all the previous memories of similar perceptions are called to active memory for comparison to the new perception in order to effect the proper response, this is equivalent to simplifying the new perception to its essentials, because its essentials are all the similar memories that share some aspect of the new perception. Once the new perception is analyzed by comparison to all the similar memories, then the mind must put all these essentials, or similar memories, together to come up with an appropriate response – the bigger picture. Everything the mind deals with is handled in this same way, which is why deductive and inductive logic are essential to our existence.

Each mind is unique. There is no way that anyone can actually see a situation from someone else's perspective because no one has the same memories that anyone else has, and it's our memories that give us our perspective and our feeling of "self." Our mind is only aware of our own brain. There is no possible way one person's mind can have first-hand knowledge of anything that is taking place in someone else's mind. When someone says, "I know how you feel," this can really be nothing more than meaningless words or consolation because it is impossible to know how another person feels. On the other side of the coin, it's also impossible not to know how you, yourself, feel.

Out-of-body experiences are often attributed to some mystical process of the mind that can't be explained if the mind is nothing more than just a part of the brain. However, these episodes have been shown by experiment to be an easily explainable product of an abnormal function of the brain. By stimulating the temporal lobes of the brain with a transcranial magnetic stimulator (TMS), the function of which was explained in a previous chapter, experimenters were able to repeatedly reproduce out-of-body experiences, such as floating above the bed or sinking into the bed, for example. These experiences have also been shown to occur when a person has low blood sugar, sudden decreases in oxygen, and stressful events. When one part of the brain is abnormally stimulated with TMS or some pathological condition, it can cause erroneous information to be transmitted to other parts of the brain which then misinterpret that information, resulting in the mind being fooled into thinking that something exists which actually doesn't. In other words, these are illusions. There have been reported cases of unconscious patients in hospitals who, when they regained consciousness, told their doctors that they were able to perceive things very clearly that they wouldn't have been able to perceive in their unconscious state, and that they were able to hear and recall things accurately that the hospital staff did and said while these patients were unconscious. And all of this took place while the patients were floating above the bed during out-of-body experiences during the unconscious state. Although this may sound very convincing, it is much more likely that these patients were really not unconscious during these episodes. In my experience as a neurologist, I have been consulted numerous times to examine patients in intensive care units of hospitals for the purpose of determining their brain status. More often than not, when patients are described as being unconscious, I have found during my neurological examination that the diagnosis of unconsciousness is in error and that they are at least conscious enough that they can see or hear some of what's going on around them. It can often be very difficult to determine whether someone is truly unconscious or not, and even when someone who is specifically trained in this area makes that determination, errors are still likely to be made. It is much easier for a patient with a decreased level of consciousness to consciously receive perceptions than it is for him to respond to those perceptions so that others can determine he is conscious.

At what point, in removing successive parts of the mind, does a person stop being "that" person? (This question assumes that one associates who a person is with his brain only, rather than with any of his other organ systems like the heart, lungs, blood, and liver.) As you may have guessed by now, only the person himself can determine when he is no longer himself. No one else can decide this because no one else can have any first-hand knowledge about what takes place within that person's mind. And because each person's mind is different from every-one else's, each person will have his own idea of when he is no longer himself. In other words, we can't say that a person will no longer be himself when seventy percent of his brain ceases to function, or when ninety percent of it ceases to function. It would be different for everyone. For instance, when people get Alzheimer's disease, those who were highly educated before the onset of the disease can lose more than ninety percent of their memory function before they can no longer think or know themselves, while those with little education may lose the abil-ity to think or know themselves after losing just seventy percent of their memory function. Ironically, even though each person himself is the only one who can determine when he is no longer himself, once he reaches the point when he is no longer himself, he will have lost the ability to know that he's no longer himself. Nevertheless, he is still the only person qualified to make this determination.

CONSCIOUSNESS

Depending on whether you are talking to a philosopher or a neuroscientist, consciousness has two very different meanings. There have been attempts to combine the meaning of con-sciousness for these two groups to come up with one workable definition that both groups can be satisfied with. These have included seminars and conferences where experts from both fields have come together to discuss various points about consciousness for days at a time. At this time, however, a consensus of agreement has not been established.

Neuroscience Approach

For a neuroscientist, consciousness is completely contained within the brain itself. Consciousness is simply defined as being able to conceive the subjective flow of time (as described in the chapter on "time.") This means that someone who is conscious is aware of the "present". A conscious person can receive a time-ordered sequence of perceptions through one or more of his five senses, compare those perceptions to memories of similar time-ordered perceptions stored in his brain, form a concept of the flow of time from them, then make a response to those incoming perceptions based on what is dictated by this analysis. If you can't do this, you're not conscious. If you can do it, you are conscious. Of course, there are degrees of consciousness, just as there are degrees of brightness of a light, for example. For someone who has just suffered a heart attack with a resulting compromised blood flow to the brain, he may only be able to hear and understand a few words that you say to him and would have an obvious decreased level of consciousness. But as long as his brain is able to process any new sensory information while aware of a time line, he has some degree of consciousness.

Who determines whether someone is conscious or not? Usually it's obvious whether someone is conscious or not just by observing him. But sometimes a person may appear to be conscious even though he isn't. For instance, if you observe a person sleepwalking, you will see that he interacts with his environment like someone who is conscious. He may get out of bed, walk to the door, open it, and then walk outside. But because he is not aware of the subjective flow of time, he is not conscious. The only person who knows for sure if someone is conscious is that person himself. There are no tests available that can determine with certainty whether someone is absolutely conscious or absolutely unconscious. As with just about everything else concerning each individual brain, each brain itself also determines whether it is conscious.

If consciousness is determined by the brain itself, how does the brain know when it's unconscious, since it has to be conscious to be aware of what's going on with itself? The answer is that the brain doesn't need to be aware of itself in order to function, so consciousness doesn't matter. The brain doesn't know when it's unconscious, nor does it care. It is only aware of itself and its state of consciousness when it *is* conscious – that is, when it is receiving perceptions and is aware of the flow of time associated with receiving them. If this seems strange, keep in mind that consciousness is something that we, as goal-oriented humans, have attached significant importance to because it plays a major role in our "quality of life." But to our brain as a whole, in its role as a living machine, consciousness is just something that developed as a part of its existence. A vast amount of what goes on in the brain doesn't even require us to be conscious. If we slept for twenty-three hours per day instead of eight hours per day, our brain would be perfectly content with this arrangement. In fact, if we were able to provide ourselves with nourishment somehow while we were sleeping, our brain would still function quite well even if we were never conscious. As one of our many organ systems, it functions just as well to keep our bodies alive and working properly when it's unconscious as when it's conscious. It's only requirement for survival is a continuous supply of glucose, which is the only fuel it uses to run all its "machinery." For the brain as a whole, if there were one hundred functions that were associated with it, and consciousness was number eight, it would have no more importance for the functioning of the brain than function number seven or number nine. We just attach more significance to consciousness because it is responsible for our "humanness," which involves interacting with other humans, seeking goals, enjoying a good meal, and whatever else makes us happy. We attach importance to consciousness because it's what makes our life worth living. Without it, we could possibly adapt and still survive like any organism that uses only stimulus/response mechanisms, but we would certainly have no quality to our life, as we know it.

This brings up another question. If our brain functions just as well whether it's conscious or not, regarding its ability to maintain our body's healthy state, and we are a product of what goes on in our brain, how can consciousness be so important to us? The answer is that as we were evolving and the brain was becoming more and more complex, to the point where we became aware of our surroundings, or we became conscious, everything changed for us as developing humans. Our lives became much more meaningful because we could voluntarily interact with our surroundings instead of just exhibiting automatic responses to various stimuli like one-celled bacteria do. The development of consciousness gave us vastly greater flexibility because it allowed the freedom to make choices. So now that we became conscious, and new horizons were opened for us, the state of being conscious enabled our brain to *choose* consciousness as something positive in our life. Notice that I used the word "choose", which means it wasn't necessarily something required for our survival, from an evolutionary standpoint, but something that we've decided affects our life in a positive manner. For example, fifteen years ago, if you wanted to talk with someone who was not near you, you looked for a pay phone, put a quarter in the slot, and called him. Everyone was content with this means of communication and it worked very well. Now, everyone has a cell phone and most people couldn't imagine not being able to call someone at any instant, no matter where they happened to be. The standard has changed so that we expect to be able to contact anyone within a few seconds from anywhere in the world. The invention of the cell phone has created its own necessity. Consciousness is very similar. That is, consciousness is theoretically not necessary for the brain's continuous functioning to keep the body alive, but once it developed, and made our lives much more interesting, we wouldn't want to live without it.

If someone lost the use of all five of his senses, could he be conscious? The answer is that he could not. In order for consciousness to exist, one must be able to evaluate incoming perceptions to the brain in such a way that he can conceive a flow of time. This would not be possible if a person had none of his five senses because he could not receive any perceptions. He may be able to move, much like a sleepwalker would do, or he might be able to dream, much as a person asleep would do, but he could not be conscious.

Philosophical Approach

For a philosopher, consciousness is not completely con-tained within the brain itself. It is more than just the electrical currents traveling from one wire to another throughout the brain. For them, consciousness exists outside the brain as well as inside. Some have attached consciousness to force fields that exist outside the brain, not unlike the magnetic fields we've dis-cussed previously. The brain can tune into these force fields like someone tunes in a radio station, in order to achieve differ-ent levels of consciousness. These consciousness force fields are said to be present whether there is a brain to tune them in or not. For philosophers, the hardest problem to deal with about consciousness is how physical processes in the brain give rise to "subjective experience," which they feel is more than just per-ceptions that are dealt with by the brain. They distinguish this from the "easy" problem, which consists of the neural mecha-nisms behind perception, how we pay attention, and the differ-ences between waking and sleep. I suspect that "subjective ex-perience" is hard for philosophers to accept as being completely within the functioning of the brain itself because it is difficult to accept the fact that we really are definable as human beings by the sum total of the mechanical processes that take place within our brain. We would like to think something more exists that makes us stand out from everything else contained within the universe – something that makes us more "mysterious." The more research that is being done on the brain, however, the more certain it is becoming that we really are nothing more than the sum of our "parts".

Some philosophers argue that consciousness does not exist at all. In these cases, the problem appears to be one of semantics, because consciousness, in these cases, is described differently than the ability to conceive the flow of time from a time-ordered set of perceptions. If the neuroscientific definition of consciousness is applied, it is obvious that consciousness does exist.

Philosophers ask why we should be conscious of ourselves. There is no profound or mysterious reason for this. We are conscious of ourselves simply because our brain happened to develop this ability. It does make our life more enjoyable, but if our brain had never developed to the point where we were conscious, we'd never know what we were missing. This is similar to the cell phone example used earlier. Cell phones make our life easier, but if they'd never been developed, we wouldn't know what we were missing, so we wouldn't be any worse off without them.

It is possible to split the two halves of the neocortex part of the brain down the center without causing the death of a person. In fact, this is occasionally done by neurosurgeons to prevent seizures in epileptic patients from spreading from one side of the brain to the other side. This helps to prevent the more violent grand mal type seizures. It has been proposed that splitting the brain in this way results in two separate ways of dealing with perceived information and association effects, one in the right hemisphere and one in the left hemisphere, resulting in two separate spheres of consciousness. Although the two halves of the neocortex hold most of the higher functioning areas of the brain, incoming and outgoing electrical impulses must travel through the more primitive lower parts of the brain and brainstem too, which cannot be split. Because of this, there could never be two separate seats of consciousness in any brain.

Even though a person with a split neocortex would work out problems differently using either the right or left half of his brain without communication between the two halves, consciousness would be determined by having at least one half of the brain awake. The person would still be aware of himself as the same person whether he was using the right, left, or both halves of his brain at any particular time.

REALITY

Reality has been discussed for centuries. There is an entire branch of philosophy called metaphysics that deals with it. Like so many other subjects that have been discussed at length, reality has also been described at various times as an illusion, something that we can never obtain any information about, something that exists independent of us, and so on.

As simplistic as it may sound, reality refers to what is real. Because of this, it has to refer to what we can perceive, and consequent to that, it may sometimes also refer to what we can conceive. As I've mentioned so many times before, if we can't perceive it, it doesn't exist for us. And if it doesn't exist for us, it's not real. Since the brain is what decides if something can be perceived or not, then the brain is ultimately responsible for deciding what's real, or what reality is. So far, this should seem straightforward and logical. But now a problem arises – *whose* brain decides what is real? We already know that everyone perceives things at least a little differently than everyone else, so it stands to reason that we may not all perceive the same thing as real. We put people in psychiatric hospitals when they see people who supposedly aren't real, or hear voices that supposedly aren't real, so it would seem that some brains are more capable of determining what's real, or what reality is, than other brains are. But what if there are fifty people who hear voices that supposedly aren't real or see people who supposedly aren't real, and only one person doesn't hear the voices or see the people. Is it now as easy to declare that the voices or sightings aren't real? The answer is that it is not. Reality is subjective. It is determined by each individual brain, and it can only be determined within the frame of reference of the person who perceives it. In other words, if you see me walking down the street carrying on a conversation just as if someone were walking beside me, but you don't see anyone there, you're reality is that there's something psychologically wrong with me because I'm talking to an imaginary person just as if he were real. On the other hand, my reality is that I am talking to a friend who is right there walking beside me. I ask him questions to which he responds in his usual voice. When my friend departs, I may shake hands with him and perceive his sweaty palm against mine, but when you observe this, you see me shaking hands with the air. For me, the reality of this situation is that my friend exists right now in the present. Your reality is that my friend does not exist right now in the present. Whose reality is correct, yours or mine? You may decide to confront me and say that there is no other person with me, and punch the air where he is supposed to be standing to show me that there's no one there. My response to your gesture is to tell you that you just injured my friend by punching him, and now his nose is bleeding. After cursing at you, I help my friend over to a bench and struggle to stop his nose from bleeding. Beads of sweat start forming on my brow from the exertion of helping my friend to the bench, and I am breathing noticeably faster from this exertion. I also see drops of blood on my clothes that dripped from my friend's nose as I was helping him to the bench. You continue trying to convince me that I'm imagining my friend and everything associated with him, while I try to convince you that he is real. I'm wondering why you are playing this cruel joke on me and my friend, while you are wondering what psychiatric hospital I must have escaped from. The point of all this is to show that reality is relative to each brain's frame of reference. In this example, what you perceive as reality is no more "correct" than what I perceive as reality. If I perceive that my friend exists, and that now he has a bloody nose, and that the handkerchief he uses to wipe his nose is now wet with blood, then that is reality for me. If you perceive none of this, and punch at the air where you feel nothing, then that is your reality. We each perceive the same event differently, but what each of our brains perceives is what is real for each brain. Remember that all a brain can do is work with what electrical signals it receives from the peripheral receptors for our five senses. If your brain interprets the signals coming from your sensory receptors to indicate no person standing near me, then that's how the new memories for this event will be recorded in your brain. If my brain interprets the signals coming from my sensory receptors to indicate that my friend is standing near me, and that he's carrying on a conversation with me, then that's how the new memories for this event will be recorded in my brain. If you and I were the only two people on earth, neither one of us would likely be able to convince the other that what we perceived was what "really" existed. There is no "really" here, because there is no universal standard for reality. What I perceive is true reality for me, and what you perceive is true reality for you. We have different frames of reference because we have different

stored memories in our brains that we compare the new perceptions about my friend to, in order to come up with an appropriate response. In my case, when I talk to my friend, my brain is
either receiving signals from my auditory sensory receptors that
convey the sounds of words that my friend is using to respond
to me, *or* my brain is erroneously activating old memories about
conversations I've had in the past with my friend and presenting
them to active working memory as false "new" perceptions that
fool my brain's processing mechanisms into thinking they actually are new perceptions being received in my brain, which fool
my brain into thinking that my friend is actually there beside
me. Either way, my brain perceives my friend as reality. In
your case, when you see me talking to what you perceive as an
imaginary person, your brain is either receiving signals from
your visual receptors that convey no evidence of a person
standing next to me, *or* your brain is erroneously activating old
memories related to seeing me walk down the street by myself
and presenting them to active working memory as false "new"
perceptions that fool your brain's processing mechanisms into
thinking they actually are new perceptions being received in
your brain, which fool your brain into thinking that my friend is
not there beside me. Either way, your brain perceives my friend
as imaginary, and that is your reality.

Now let's suppose that you and I are not the only two people on the earth, and that you gather fifty people who agree with
you that my friend is imaginary. You all approach me and try
to convince me that my friend is not real. After listening to all
of you for several hours, I finally am convinced that my friend
is not real. Why does this happen? In this case, it is because I
am receiving a constant flow of new perceptions from you and

the other fifty people about my friend being imaginary. With all these new "imaginary friend" perceptions being received in my brain, I start making some memories of my own from them (if they are convincing enough) that will now be activated and used as similar memories to perceptions about my friend's existence. When these newly formed memories of his nonexistence are used for comparison to new perceptions from my friend, they cause my brain to respond that my friend is not real. In other words, the perceptions I received from you and the other fifty people were strong enough that they were able to replace the memories that were being activated by my brain previously, which "told" my brain that the friend was real. However, if my memories were strong enough about my friend's existence, no amount of convincing by you and the other fifty people would be likely to replace them, and I would continue to believe that my friend actually existed – and in this case, my friend's existence would remain absolutely real in my frame of reference. But suppose the opposite scenario occurred. What if I found fifty people whose reality was that my friend did exist, and they then tried to convince you that he really did exist? If they were very convincing, and caused strong memories to form in your brain that he truly did exist, then you might then use those memories to compare to new perceptions about my friend and now your new memories would "tell" your brain that the friend was real. Now your reality would be that my friend did exist. There is no universal standard of reality. Reality is entirely determined within each person's brain and for each person's frame of reference. It may or may not agree with someone else's reality, but if it does not agree with someone else's reality, it is no less real than his reality. We can try to change what one person perceives or conceives as reality, and if we're successful, then reality truly does change in that person's frame of reference. But if we're unsuccessful in changing that person's perception or conception of reality, it doesn't make his reality any less real than ours or our group's. In other words, although we do most things democratically, or by majority rule, and try to get others to conform to the majority viewpoint for harmony's sake, reality is not what the majority of people agree it is. It is what each individual perceives it to be.

There are probably those who are still thinking that if two people perceive the same event in an entirely different way, there must be some way to prove who is right and who is wrong. That would be faulty thinking though, because first, as was mentioned earlier, there is no universal standard for the reality of an event because each brain decides what's real and each brain is different. Also remember that no one's brain is any more important for deciding reality than anyone else's brain, which means that there is no way to prove whose interpretation of reality is "correct." Second, if one brain perceives some event in a certain way, this means that particular brain evaluated the event using everything it had available in its memory banks for comparison and evaluation of a new perception and came up with what it perceived was the reality of that new perception. Since no one can have any first hand knowledge of what's going on in someone else's brain, because everyone is completely isolated regarding his individual brain functioning, then no one can say that what he perceives as reality is what reality has to be for anyone else. For instance, I may believe that because my arms are roughly shaped like birds' wings, I can fly. I start flapping my arms and perceive that I am flying because when my brain perceives the flapping of my arms, then compares these perceptions to memories of similar perceptions, which convey that flapping arms is equal to flying, my brain's response to these incoming perceptions of my arms flapping is that I am truly flying. I may then go up on the top of my roof and fly off, perceiving that I am truly flying. If I survive this "flight" from my roof, the reality of the situation for my brain will be that I truly was flying, but that I made a bad landing and just need more practice. In my frame of reference, my reality is that I can fly. Whether someone else's reality agrees with mine makes no difference. My reality is that I was truly flying and that's all that matters in my frame of reference. There is no "correct" or "incorrect" reality, and there is no "majority" reality.

There have been diagnostic studies used on the brain, such as fMRI or PET scanning, which are ways of determining which parts of the brain are being used when certain tasks are performed or certain thoughts are evoked. If the scanner operator asks the patient about his mother, he might notice that a certain part of the patient's brain lights up when he's thinking about his mother. The patient might then respond that his mother is right there in the scanning room with him, and the operator might notice another part of the brain light up as well. But even though the operator doesn't see anyone else in the room with him and the patient, he cannot tell from looking at the activity going on in the patient's brain scan whether the patient's mother was actually there in the patient's presence. In other words, even though he is probing the deepest parts of the patient's brain, he cannot tell what the patient's reality is because he cannot get into the frame of reference of the patient. No one can enter another person's frame of reference for reality. A person might be able to change another person's frame of reference for

reality to more closely match his own, using convincing argu-
ments, but he can never actually enter another person's frame of
reference for reality. (This will be seen again in the chapter on
religion.)

Philosophers Hegel, Marx, and Sartre, for example, believed
that what counts is the way our brain interprets or understands
things, not "the way things actually are." The problem with this
is that although it leaves reality up to the individual, it assumes
there is a universal standard of reality, as referred to by the term
"the way things actually are." This is in error because there is
no "way things actually are." Things "are" the way each brain
perceives them – nothing more and nothing less. To prove this,
suppose you were the only person in the universe and you saw a
little green alien with two heads and purple spots standing in
front of you. You reach out to touch him and you feel his rub-
bery skin. In your frame of reference for reality, this alien is
real. Could there possibly be a universal standard of reality to
show that this alien is not real, given that you are the only human being in the universe and there's no one who could refute
the existence of the little green alien? The answer is that there
could not be. It would make no logical sense to come to any
other conclusion. Would adding more human beings to the universe automatically create a universal standard of reality to
compare your sighting to, especially if they disagreed with you
about the existence of the green alien? If it did, that would be
equivalent to saying that their brains were more important than
yours for determining reality because their presence suddenly
dictated a universal standard for reality. This wouldn't make
logical sense either. Therefore, there can be no universal stan-

dard for reality, and each person's reality is real in his frame of reference.

One of the problems with getting rid of a universal standard for reality is that we are used to a majority rule, and usually go along with what the majority says is true, even if we don't necessarily agree. The universal standard is usually considered to be what the majority agrees upon. Oftentimes, we will convince ourselves that what we are thinking has to be wrong because it doesn't agree with the majority viewpoint, and they can't all be wrong. So we change our thoughts about the situation to agree with the majority viewpoint, and even convince ourselves that our previous viewpoint was actually incorrect. The underlying thought is that if you get enough people to believe something, it becomes the standard. Although this has been demonstrated to occur over and over throughout history, it does not indicate that there is a universal standard of reality that we can compare all perceptions to in order to determine which are real and which are not.

Because of the way our brain functions, it is theoretically possible that all of our memories could have formed spontaneously without any perceptive input, and that none of what we remember by recalling old memories ever really occurred. The same could be said for events we think we are actively perceiving. They could just be spontaneous electrical signals being sent to the brain from our sensory receptors that the brain interprets as external events occurring in the present. If this were the case, we might say that reality doesn't "really" exist. But then we'd be wrong again because, as has been mentioned several times, reality is what each individual brain perceives as real. It doesn't matter if it's all just abnormal signals in the brain or actual signals from external events. It's what the brain interprets as real right now in the present that determines whether it is real or not. If the brain's interpretation of what's real changes five minutes later, based on new information, then that new interpretation becomes what's real.

How are the past, present, and future related to reality? What I may perceive as reality now, in the present, may change in the future after new information convinces me otherwise. Or my present realities may change what I thought were realities in the past. From this, it can be concluded that realities are dynamic rather than static. They can change with more perceptions, or more information. They are not bound to the past, present, or future, but can exist in all three periods, and often change across time periods. This is because the brain itself is dynamic rather than static, with new memories constantly being formed and compared to old memories, while old memories can change with age, resulting in different memories than what were actually experienced when they originally formed. For instance, I may have driven a black car forty years ago, but over the past forty years the specific memory identifying my car as being black has deteriorated just enough to where it's now shaped into a form that codes for a green car. I would never know that the memory changed because the memory for the black car no longer exists in my brain. When I recall the car I had, I'll swear it was green, and that's my reality for the color of that car now.

The most important point to remember about reality is that it is subjective, or individualized to each person's brain. No one's perception or conception of reality is any more valid than anyone else's, and the only reality that ultimately matters for each person is the one that exists in his brain.

LEARNING, INTELLIGENCE, AND KNOWLEDGE

When we learn something, a change has to occur in our brain that makes it different than it was before the act of learning took place. This change that occurs is the formation of a permanent memory that can be activated later for comparison to new perceptions so that a better-informed response to the new perceptions can be made. Learning enables predicting what will happen in the future by recalling what occurred in the past. If the significance of life is change, then learning is the brain's way of recording those changes. Learning is simply the formation of permanent memories from perceptions that we experience. If someone is incapable of forming memories, he is incapable of learning. Also, if a person is incapable of perceiving, as would occur if he had none of his five senses, he would also be incapable of learning.

Research on the brain shows that we learn much more from our mistakes than from our successes. Why would this be? The reason is because successes don't usually have the potential to harm us, but failures can have catastrophic results that might affect our survival. Let's say you are on a hunting trip and the guide offers you a choice of guns to use for shooting a bear. You choose one of them at random and then take off into the wild. Before long, you come face to face with a huge bear. You aim your gun at the bear and pull the trigger, but nothing happens. Luckily for you, one of your friends happens to be near and shoots the bear before it can attack you. This perception of your gun failing to fire forms a very strong memory in your brain for later recall, because it is important for your survival. The next time you go bear hunting, you will certainly be sure not to choose the same kind of gun that failed to fire, or you will be apt to try out whichever gun you choose to make sure it works before you start hunting. If your original gun had fired properly though, you probably would not have formed a very strong memory of what type gun you used, and would be just as likely to pick that model gun as any other model from the group offered to you by the guide the next time you go bear hunting. You also would probably not feel compelled to try it out first to make sure it worked.

Memories that are formed in the process of learning are not all created equally, as the previous example demonstrates. The strength of each memory formed is directly related to its importance for our well-being. The stronger a memory is, the easier it is to recall it, and the more likely it is to be recalled for comparison with new perceptions arriving in the brain, even if it is only remotely related to the incoming perception. For instance, if I have a greater fear of snakes than you do, I am much more likely to recoil in fear from a twig lying on the ground than you are, because when the perception of seeing the twig arrives in my brain for comparison to previous memories to initiate a response, the fact that the twig even remotely resembles a snake will cause my strong memories of snakes to be recalled for comparison to the twig, and my response will be to jump away. Since you are not afraid of snakes, you are less likely to have any strongly recorded memories of snakes, so your snake memories won't be recalled when you see the twig, and you won't jump away from it. The reason you and I have such different memories associated with snakes is because somewhere in my past, I must have had a bad experience with a snake that caused my strong memories of snakes to be formed, or learned, while in your past, there was no bad experience with snakes, so you don't have strong memories of them.

As children, most of us spent a lot of time memorizing various written works for school. We've memorized the Pledge of Allegiance, parts of the Declaration of Independence, the Bill of Rights, poems, and whatever else our teachers could find. Why was that so important? The reason is that when we were children, our brains had many more wires and connections than they do as adults. If those wires weren't used for something, like storing lots of memories, they would eventually be diminished and we would have fewer of them to work with as adults. By performing memorization exercises as children, we preserve much more of our brain capacity and ensure that when we're adults, we will have an optimum brain capacity.

Intelligence can be thought of as taking learning one step farther along. Learning is forming new memories of perceptions that one experiences, but intelligence is using those stored memories of perceptions to form new concepts, which can then be stored as permanent memories also. Intelligence depends on learned information as a starting point, but then modifies those memories of learned information to come up with some new concept that has not been perceived through any of the five senses. That is, intelligence occurs entirely within the confines of the brain itself. All the changes in the brain that are associated with intelligence start inside the brain and end inside the brain without ever sending any electric impulses to any of the other wires outside the brain. "Solving problems," "thinking," and "planning" are terms that refer to this process of taking memories of perceptions and modifying them to come up with new concepts. People who have a greater capacity for modifying memories of perceptions have more intelligence than people who don't have this increased capacity. It has been found experimentally that people can actually train their brains to be better able to convert memories of perceptions to new concepts (increase their intelligence) by using mental exercises, such as doing thought puzzles or playing games like chess that require more thought.

What takes place in the brain to cause new concepts to form from the recorded memories of perceptions when someone is actively using his intelligence? As you may recall, when a perception is stored as a permanent memory in the brain, it is not put in a little compartment or anything like that. It is simply stored as a modification in a few of the wires in the brain so that any time an electric impulse travels along those exact wires that were activated and modified when the forming memory first traveled along those wires, the memory of the same event that was perceived the first time the electric current traveled down those wires will be reactivated, or brought into active memory. Stronger memories involve more wires so that they can be found and triggered more easily. The brain's wiring and connections are largely random, so when a memory is being formed, it just chooses the wires for memory formation that it happens to be passing along at the time and then makes more branch connections to that particular area to make sure that it can "pull in" electric current more easily when it comes time to activate that particular memory by running an electric current through that area. To conceptualize, or use your intelligence, you may activate different combinations of stored memories at one time, and then send electric impulses down parts of each of these memories at the same time. By doing this, you create a new electrical pathway that has parts of several old memories included in it. This combination of parts of old memories can create a new memory, or concept, and can now be stored as a new memory of a concept if your brain thinks it's worth keeping and storing. You may wonder how the brain knows just which parts of the old memories it should use to form the new concept. The brain doesn't know which parts to use. It just keeps sending impulses down various branches of combinations of the memories it has recalled until it finds a combination that gives a correct answer to the problem. That's why sometimes we have to think for so long before we come up with an acceptable solution to a problem. People with more intelligence are better able to activate and integrate branches of different stored memories to come up with new concepts than people with less intelligence. Since the brain is so much more adaptable in children than in adults, it is much more critical for reaching maximum intelligence that children perform mental exercises than waiting until they are adults.

On television game shows where contestants are asked trivia questions, and the more correct answers they give, the more money they win, we often hear that the big winners are very intelligent. Is that really the case? Those contestants have learned a lot of information, but they may or may not be intelligent. Remember that learning is the forming of new memories of perceptions, but intelligence is using those memories of perceptions to form new concepts within the brain itself. When someone answers a trivia question, he is recalling memories of perceptions; he is not forming new concepts within his brain. So the correct statement would be that the person who is able to answer more trivia questions has learned more than the other contestants, but is not necessarily more intelligent.

A prodigy is a person who is especially gifted at something. Do prodigies have a higher capacity for learning or a higher intelligence? Although they can have both, they are usually gifted with a higher intelligence in their particular field. That is, their contributions to their areas of expertise usually involve new, creative, or conceptual information rather than a larger capacity for learning information already known about their field. We don't hear of geography or history prodigies because these fields require learning and memorization for expertise, rather than the ability to conceptualize. We more often hear about musical or math prodigies because after the simple basics of each of these fields are learned, these fields require conceptualization in order for one to stand out from others in the same field.

Knowledge generally refers to both learning and intelligence. It is not as specific as either learning or intelligence, and is more often used in a philosophical context. In fact, there is an entire field of philosophy called epistemology that deals with the subject of knowledge. Epistemological questions about knowledge might ask whether knowledge really exists, whether we can really know anything at all, and whether knowledge exists outside of the brain. These are questions that have been debated for at least a few thousand years, but with the relatively recent progress that has been made in the science of how the brain works, these questions, like the philosophical questions about consciousness, have been relegated to topics of conversation at cocktail parties more than as serious alternatives to what scientific discovery has shown to be factual, regarding learning and intelligence.

EMOTION AND LOGIC

Emotion and logic are dealt with together here because they are the basis for all the memories that are stored in our brain and they often seem to be the antithesis of each other. When incoming perceptions are recorded as memories in our brain, they may be recorded as purely logical memories, such as math problems, purely emotional memories, such as anger, or a combination with logical and emotion components, such as a fear of snakes because of being bitten by one in the past. We will first discuss what emotion is, how it is stored in the brain, and what effects it has on our thoughts and actions, and then we will discuss logic.

Emotional memories are very strong memories. That is, an emotional memory is stored in the brain in such a way that not only can it be very easily located and recalled for comparison to new perceptions arriving in the brain, but it is also stored so that it is not as likely to be degraded over time. Emotions are simply more strongly formed memories.

Most researchers who study emotions consider six personal (primary) emotions, and four social (secondary) emotions. The personal emotions are happiness, sadness, anger, surprise, disgust, and fear. The social emotions are envy, guilt, pride, and embarrassment. Personal emotions are those one would experience even if there were no other people living in the universe, while social emotions require an interaction with at least one other person to manifest themselves.

We might wonder what it is about the different emotions that causes all of them to be recorded as such strong memories in the brain. It was mentioned earlier that the brain pays the most attention to perceptions that can affect our survival, or well-being, and records these as much stronger memories than those that don't affect these things. If we analyze all ten of the emotions mentioned above to determine if there is something in particular about all of them that might cause the brain to store them as very strong memories, we notice that each one deals with feeling "secure" and "in control" – or the lack of these feelings. When we don't feel secure, or we don't feel like we're in control of a situation, that is when memories of emotions are most likely to be activated in order to initiate a response dictated by a new perception the brain is evaluating. Feeling secure or in control is certainly related to survival, so when a new perception arrives in the brain relating to our security, it's important to activate a memory that was formed because it had the potential of affecting our survival when faced with that similar type of new perception. For instance, you may be out in a small boat in the middle of a lake with your child, and he stands up in the boat, nearly causing it to capsize. You may immediately become surprised, because this was something that you were not expecting, and the brain always wants to make strong memories of perceptions that are not what is expected so that it can prevent them in the future. You may also feel fear, because if the boat capsized, there's a chance you and your child could both drown. This would also cause a strong memory to be recorded for obvious reasons. Finally, you may also feel anger, either directed at yourself because you forgot to tell your child not to stand up in the boat, or at your child because you told him not to stand up when you began your boat ride, but he did it anyway. The anger you feel must be recorded as a strong memory because it needs to be recalled the next time you go out in a boat so that you are either more likely to remember to tell your child not to stand up if you forgot to the first time, or are more adamant about telling your child not to stand up in the boat if you told him the first time but he didn't listen to you.

Of the six personal emotions we feel, "happiness" is the only one that could be considered a positive emotion. The other five are elicited by potentially harmful perceptions. It was mentioned that the brain usually only makes strong memories of potentially harmful perceptions because those are the ones that affect our survival. So why should the brain make strong memories of an emotion like happiness, which is seemingly not necessary for survival? The reason is because happiness actually *is* necessary for our survival, but in a more indirect way. When memories of the more negative emotions are recalled because they are similar to a new perception arriving in the brain, they send electric impulses to other parts of the brain that can start a cascade of chemicals to be released from those other areas of the brain in anticipation of what the body has to do next, once the new perception occurred that triggered the negative emotion. These chemicals are released in anticipation of a possible "fight or flight" response to prepare the body to respond to the perceived threat to survival. For instance, if you're walking through the woods and a lion jumps out in front of you, the two emotions you will activate in your brain associated with this perception are fear and surprise. Once activated, they will send a secondary electric signal to trigger an adrenaline release in your brain that will make your heart beat faster to carry more oxygen and fuel to your legs where it will be needed when you start running away. It will also cause the arteries to constrict in your abdomen to divert the blood away from there and towards your legs and arms instead so that if you need to fight the lion, you will have more strength to do so. If the only emotions you had were strong negative emotions, there would be a constant release of at least some of these "fight or flight" chemicals nearly all the time because we don't go for very long without some kind of a new perception that is associated with an emotion. This would create long-term problems because all of these chemicals have bad effects on the body when they are circulating continuously. They can cause chronic high blood pressure, strokes, heart problems, and diabetes. Fortunately, when emotional memories for happiness are activated by the brain, these memories also have connections to the areas of the brain that trigger the release of the "fight or flight" chemicals, but instead of turning them on, these connections from the happiness memories shut them off, thus counteracting the effects of the negative emotions. So if the memories of the emotions that turn them on are very strongly formed, then the memories for the emotion that turns them off must be equally as strong in order to counteract their effects. For example, people who are chronically depressed because of losing a loved one or because of some other tragedy, and who have absolutely no happiness at all in their lives over a long period of time, often develop many of the medical problems mentioned above. When one of the spouses of a long-married elderly couple dies, it is not uncommon to see the other spouse die within a few weeks. This is because of the constant recall to memory of the strong emotion of sadness that then triggers the release of adrenaline, which constricts the blood vessels that are already corroded with age, and this results in a stroke or a heart attack.

The secondary, or social, emotions also deal with feeling secure or in control, or with survival, but this is survival within the "group," rather than personal survival. Like the primary emotions, they are all negative except one. Envy, guilt, and embarrassment cause the release of the same chemicals mentioned above for the "fight or flight" response, and pride, the only positive social emotion, causes these chemicals to be turned off to prevent the chronic problems associated with their continued release from the brain.

Other emotions, like "love" and "hate," also cause the formation of very strong memories, just as all emotions do, but are not considered primary emotions because they are not essential for survival of an individual. Some people go through life without ever forming any emotional memories related to love or hate, but no one goes through life without forming memories related to all six of the primary emotions. We don't know for sure why love is a strong emotion but there are some good theories that relate it indirectly, on an evolutionary basis, to survival of our species rather than survival of an individual. That is, if there is a strong bond of love between two people, it usually results in offspring, and the offspring are more likely to thrive if both parents are there to take care of them. Also, a strong bond of love is important between parents and offspring in order that the offspring are nurtured and ultimately survive. The emotion of hate usually activates the primary emotions of anger, sadness, disgust, and possibly fear, which may indicate that hate forms strong memories because it is secondarily associated with survival by activating some of the primary emotional memories, but since hate is not an emotion that everyone experiences, it is not a primary emotion itself.

Logic is at the other end of the spectrum from emotion. Permanent memories formed in the brain of purely logical perceptions are not as strongly formed as emotional memories because purely logical memories are not associated with individual survival. For instance, if you are trying to figure out the proper mixture of ingredients to make laundry detergent at a soap company, you are recalling to active memory purely logical memories which have no emotional memories attached because there is no threat to your survival. However, if it is important that you mix the ingredients in the proper sequence to avoid blowing up the lab, then there is an emotional component of fear involved because now your survival is at stake. When a new perception is received in the brain for comparison to stored memories to dictate the correct response to that new perception, there are usually similar memories recalled from both the logical and emotional memory areas of the brain at the same time, so a purely emotional or purely logical response would not be very common. Usually, a mixture of the two is the result.

Emotional memories deal with personal security, and hence, survival. Logical memories deal with solving problems.

BELIEFS

Beliefs are memories stored in the brain, so they either have to be the results of perceptions that have been experienced, or concepts that were formed within the brain itself. Since the definition of belief centers on the inability to prove it via perception, it obviously cannot be a perception. Therefore, a belief has to be a concept that we have formed into a memory. Once various perceptions have been received in the brain, the thought process can take over to modify the memories of the various perceptions in order to come up with a new concept. If that new concept seems reasonable to the person who formed it in his brain, but he can't prove whether it exists, at least for the time being, then the new memory of that concept becomes a belief for that person. If that belief eventually is proved, it is no longer a belief but a fact. For instance, if a person is hiking in the forest and notices how beautiful all the various plants and other landscape appear, he might think that there is no way something this beautiful could have happened by chance. He thinks that there had to be some influence by a higher power to produce all these things, and so he believes that God must exist. This new concept of the existence of God he formed from his perceptions of all the beautiful sights in the forest constitutes a belief. If God should happen to appear to the person, then the new concept he formed is no longer a belief but a reality.

Beliefs are different for each person, even if those beliefs pertain to the same perception. If two people experience the same perception and then form concepts about the perception that become beliefs for each of those two people, the belief they conceive is different for each of them. The reason is because each person draws upon old memories of stored perceptions and concepts for comparison with the new perception to come up with a final concept that becomes a belief, and the old memories used for comparison will be different for each of the two people since they each have different life experiences. This means that the final concept, or belief, that results from comparing the new perception to all the similar old memories cannot possibly be exactly the same for both of them. For instance, suppose Joe and Pete are watching a baseball game. The opposing pitcher pitches the ball and it hits their hometown batter in his back. Joe and Pete both witness this event. Joe, who has always been a pessimist because nothing ever seems to go right for him, forms the belief that the pitcher threw at their batter on purpose because he was trying to injure him. Pete, who has always been an optimist because things have always seemed to go well for him, forms the belief that this was just an errant pitch and now our team is lucky because the batter gets to go to first base with a walk. The same event produced two completely different beliefs in two different brains because of their unique stored memories that were used for comparison to that event to form a new concept, or belief, about it. The implications of this are far-reaching, especially in a large society where the citizens may watch and listen to their leaders on television, then form beliefs about those perceptions.

CONSCIENCE AND RATIONALIZATION

Conscience is a strange phenomenon. It is something all people have, but it plays a more active role in decision-making for some people than for others. It only applies to our dealings with other people and with animals, but does not apply to our dealings with inanimate objects. It centers on the idea of "fairness." We all have permanent memories stored in our brains for what we consider to be the fair treatment of other people and animals, and when we don't act according to what we conceive as being fair, we have a "guilty conscience."

The word "conscience" is another one of those nebulous words like "mind" that refers more to the overall dynamics of some activity in the brain than to the makeup of one isolated part of the brain. Our conscience derives from various stored memories of perceptions and conceptions. These stored memories are found in the emotional parts of the memory system. In fact, a lot of the problems that result in a guilty conscience are caused because when a new perception is received in the brain and compared for similarities to old memories of previous perceptions and conceptions, the logical memories dictate one response to the new perception, while the emotional memories dictate a different response to the same new perception. The logical memories dictate a response that will have the best outcome for ourselves without regard for anyone or anything else. The emotional memories also dictate a response that will have the best outcome for ourselves, but only if it doesn't come at the expense of another person or animal. For instance, we've all read the stories about the hero who jumps into the raging river to save the young child who lost his footing and fell in, but can't swim. He saves the child but in the process, loses his own life. The logical memories in the hero's brain dictate that he should let the child drown because jumping into the water presents a risk to the hero's life. The emotional memories in the hero's brain dictate that because he can swim and the child can't, it is only fair that he jump in the water to save the child because it is more likely that both of them will survive if he helps than if he doesn't.

Each person's brain has a different emotional memory component that relates to the idea of fairness in the treatment of others. This is because of the types of different perceptions that each person has experienced throughout his life. Someone who was raised in a home where being helpful and not taking advantage of anyone was stressed is much more likely to have strong emotional memories that dictate being fair with everyone. Someone who was raised in a home where being helpful and not taking advantage of anyone was never mentioned nor shown by example is much more likely to have very few, if any, strong emotional memories that dictate being fair with everyone. In the latter case, the person is much less likely to respond to others in a fair manner, but more likely to respond to others in a logical, or self-serving, manner.

Why is it that conscience only applies to interactions with other people and animals? Why are animals included, and why aren't inanimate objects included? Animals are included if human beings can form some type of "bond" with them. This is because we project our own emotions onto anything that we can emotionally bond with, so if we can bond with animals, we tend to humanize them such that we project what we would feel in a particular situation onto what they must be feeling. If the animal is one that we would probably not bond with in any way, we are much less likely to consider an emotional response of fairness when dealing with it. For instance, we are much more likely to feel compelled to save a kitten that falls into the river than a cockroach that falls into the river. Since inanimate objects are clearly unfeeling, we would never elicit an emotional response from the brain in dealing with them. If a rock falls into the raging river, we wouldn't even consider jumping in to pull it out.

Even though the stored emotional memories for the sense of fairness tend to outweigh the stored logical memories for self-preservation for most people, because emotional memories are much stronger memories than logical memories, sometimes there is a conflict between the logical and emotional memories that results in two different final responses being proposed by the two systems. In these cases, where a clear response is not indicated, the brain must still make a decision on what response to make, even though it's getting conflicting information from the two sources. The logical memory system dictates what the response should be to benefit the person himself, while the emotional memory system dictates a different response that would be the most fair. For instance, you happen to be driving home from work at night after stopping at a bar for a couple of drinks. Suddenly, on a lonely stretch of road, you hit someone walking along the side of the road because you're swerving a little from the effects of the alcohol. You stop and check on the person you just hit. He's lying there on the side of the road and it is clear that he is dead. You quickly look around and feel very confident that there is no one who witnessed this accident besides you and the person you hit. You assess the situation. You can either get back in your car and leave quickly, knowing that the likelihood of your being discovered as the hit-and-run driver is almost non-existent, or you can call the police right away on your cell phone, tell them what happened, and wait there until they arrive. You realize that if you stay there, the police will surely administer the breath test for alcohol, which you won't pass, then you'll be charged with manslaughter, and you'll probably spend the next five years in prison. What do you do? In a situation like this, there's a pretty good chance that you will be getting conflicting information from the emotional memories for fairness and the logical memories for self-preservation that will make the final decision less than "unanimous" within your brain. If you let the emotional memories win out, your life will essentially be ruined, but you'll know you did the fair thing. If you let the logical memories win out, you'll probably be haunted by what you did for the rest of your life, but otherwise, your life will continue just as it was before the accident. Let's say you let the emotional memories make the response and you call the police. As far as the health of your brain is concerned, you have made the best decision. The reason is because if you don't follow the emotional response, but follow the logical response instead, electric signals from the emotional memories for fairness would continue to be sent for the emotional response to be made anyway, since they are strong memories that expect to be heeded, regardless of what the logical memories dictate the response should be. This would include sending impulses to the parts of the brain that release the "fight or flight" chemicals mentioned previously. This could go on for years, resulting in chronic high blood pressure, diabetes, strokes, and everything else these chemicals trigger in the body over the long run. Along with these chronic problems, following the logical response instead of the emotional response for fairness can also cause the emotional memories, which are strong memories, to trigger continuous, chronic electric impulses to many other areas of the brain as well, resulting in difficulty sleeping, nervousness, and even psychosis. The logical memories don't have the capacity to do all this because they are not as strongly formed and don't have the connections to the parts of the brain that release the "fight or flight" chemicals. Unlike the emotional memories, they also don't continue firing electrical signals to the response area of the brain if they are not heeded in the brain's final response to the perception of hitting the person with the car, so no "guilty conscience" can result by not following the response dictated by logical memories.

Suppose you decide to let the logical memories make the final response, and you leave the scene of the accident, but you'd like to avoid all the problems just mentioned that are associated with not letting the emotional memories for fairness make the final response. Is there a way to get around the "guilty conscience," with its associated problems, that results from not letting the emotional memories for fairness win out over the logical memories for self-preservation? The answer is that it may be possible, and that's where rationalization enters the picture.

Rationalization is a technique we use to justify a response to an event, or perception, within our brain itself. The reason we need to apply this technique in the first place is because the event our brain has perceived and then evaluated requires a response that our emotional memories and logical memories don't agree on. Our emotional memories dictate responding in a fair way and our logical memories dictate responding in a selfish way. Rationalization is almost always applied when we decide to follow the logical response at the expense of the emotional response. This makes sense because when the logical response is made at the expense of the emotional response, the emotional memories cause all the secondary problems mentioned above, including nervousness, insomnia, high blood pressure, and so on. Since those secondary problems aren't experienced when the emotional response is followed instead of the logical response, rationalization isn't necessary in those cases.

Rationalization consists of forming new "bridging" memories of concepts to try to fool the emotional response into thinking it's being followed when, in fact, the logical response is actually being followed instead of the emotional response in a situation where the emotional and logical responses dictated by a new perception are different. For instance, using our previous example of hitting the pedestrian, you decide to quickly leave the scene of the accident instead of calling the police and waiting to report what happened, because you feel certain there are no witnesses and that they will never be able to determine that you were involved if you leave right away. In order to prevent the emotional memories for fair play from continuing to send

impulses to the response centers in your brain, causing all the
secondary problems the emotional memories do when their response to an event is not followed, you form new conceptual
memories that bridge the logical response you did follow with
the emotional response you did not follow to fool the emotionally dictated response into thinking it is being followed. These
new conceptual "bridging" memories you form in your brain for
this purpose might consist of things like rationalizing that
there's really nothing to be gained by staying at the scene of the
accident because the person is already dead, so there's nothing
that could be done for him anyway. Or you might rationalize
that the pedestrian shouldn't have been walking that close to the
edge of the road without some kind of flashlight, so it's really
not your fault that you hit him, and you shouldn't be punished
for something that really wasn't your fault. These new conceptual memory bridges connect the logical memories for the
event with the emotional memories for the event in an attempt
to make them similar enough so that the response you actually
followed satisfies the criteria for both the logical and the emotional response. "Satisfies the criteria" on an electrical level in
the brain means that the new concept connects the logical response to the emotional response by allowing electrical impulses from the logical response to now feed back to where the
emotional memories are waiting to be responded to. When
these bridging electrical signals reach the emotional response
waiting to be put into affect, they inhibit them from continuing
to send signals, and shut them off, just as if the emotional response had been selected. Another way of looking at this is to
consider two tanks of water sitting side by side with a drain at
the bottom of one but no drain on the other. You want to drain

both tanks so you connect a tube from one tank to the other so they can both be emptied out the same drain. The connecting tube is equivalent to the new concept "bridging" memory formed that acts as the rationalization factor.

As most of us are probably aware from personal experience, if the emotional response for fairness is too strong for an event where a person has decided to respond logically instead, then rationalization does not work.

ALTRUISM

We've seen that our emotional memories cause us to act towards others in a way that we feel is the fairest. We've also seen that we do this because, in the long run, it is better for our mental and physical health if we treat others fairly. That is, we are still acting in our own best interest by treating others fairly. So how does altruism fit in with all this? The answer is that it doesn't. Altruism, which is defined as doing something for someone else without any regard for personal benefit, doesn't exist. There is no possible way our brain can form a response to a perception or conception that is not the most appropriate response for our own well-being. This is because our brain can have first-hand knowledge only of itself. Everything that exists, every event that occurs, and every feeling that can be felt are only relative to the frame of reference of the person who experiences them. Therefore, every response we make to any perceived or conceived event can only be relative to what is happening in our own brain and *only* in our own brain. Our brain will always dictate the response that benefits itself the most because it can only know itself.

One of the most unselfish people we have probably all heard of was Mother Teresa. In fact, her name itself is associated with benevolence and unselfishness. Don't her actions in the underprivileged countries of the world disprove the statement that altruism cannot exist? The answer is that it doesn't. When Mother Teresa was helping the poor, her response to the perceptions of seeing the needs of the people were the most appropriate responses dictated by her brain for her own mental and physical well-being. If it weren't, her brain would not have dictated those responses because her brain was only aware of itself in her own frame of reference, and therefore it could only respond to what it was aware of. There are many possible reasons why her brain chose a response to her perceptions of poor people that entailed helping them in any way she could. For instance, she may have felt that if she didn't do all she could, God would reprimand her when she came before Him after her death. To us, she went way beyond what most of us would have been willing to do to help the poor, but it doesn't matter what we think. All that mattered to her is what her own brain conceived was the correct amount of help to give to the poor. Remember, the only thing that counts to an individual brain is what's going on within that brain, not what's going on in any other brain. This is because each brain has to use the unique memories it has of previous perceptions to base its final response on. In Mother Teresa's case, she may have been taught as a child or in the convent that to do anything less than what she was doing would not be consistent with treating others in the most fair manner. Another possibility is that she may have perceived, or conceived, a vision of God that entailed His telling her to do exactly as she was doing. The point is that whatever caused her to be so giving to the poor was something that only existed in her brain and no one else's, and her brain dictated what her actions would be because it was ultimately what would benefit her the most.

PAIN

Pain exists for one purpose and one purpose only – to warn us that damage is occurring to our body. The body's nervous system exists in such a way that the wires that carry pain signals from the peripheral areas to the brain are less likely to be interrupted than any of the other information-carrying wires. When pain signals reach the brain, they take priority over any other electrical activity that happens to be going on in the brain. That's why you immediately focus on pain when it occurs and forget about whatever else you were concentrating on at the time. Pain requires an immediate response from the brain in order to minimize whatever damage is being done to the body that is triggering the receptors for pain.

In spite of the fact that it can trigger a strong emotional response, pain is not an emotion itself. Pain is a perception because we are aware of it via our five senses. An interesting irony about pain is that the brain does not form memories of pain perceptions. All pain information from around the body travels to a small area in the thalamus of the brain stem. Once it reaches the thalamus, the thalamus then sends secondary signals to certain areas in the neocortex of the brain to let it know that pain signals are being received and that the neocortex needs to decide what to do about it right away. It may seem strange that the neocortex of the brain doesn't form memories of pain perceptions like it does for all the other types of perceptions, then compare the new perceptions of pain to memories of previous similar pain memories to decide on what response it should make. There is a very good explanation why pain perceptions are not recorded as memories. Suppose you fell out of a tree and broke your leg. The pain associated with this event would probably be excruciating. If your brain formed a memory of the perception of the pain associated with breaking your leg, that would mean that you could then recall that particular pain memory into active memory in your brain just like any other memory, and you would relive that same pain, just as if it were happening all over again, every time you recalled it to active memory. Remember that memories are stored as close to how they occurred as possible, and nobody would ever want to relive the pain associated with some injury. Therefore, no memory of the actual pain associated with an event is made. Of course, a memory will be made of your falling out of the tree and break-ing your leg, and that there was pain associated with breaking your leg, but you will not form a memory of the actual percep-tion of pain itself. That's why you can't recall any pain you've ever suffered. You can recall that a certain event was associ-ated with a significant pain, but you can't recall the perception of the pain itself. The electric impulse that is triggered by the pain receptor never reaches the area of the brain that usually compares it to previous similar memories to decide on a re-sponse. It is intercepted at the thalamus and modified so that when it is sent to the decision-making area of the neocortex of the brain, it will be recognized as pain but won't be recorded as a memory of the actual pain perception.

There is some ability to train the brain to be more tolerant of pain. On a neurological level, this is done by growing more inhibitory wires in the brain and spinal cord that connect to the pain wires, effectively decreasing their numbers and intensity.

Pain receptors exist just about everywhere in the body in some form or another. One of the few places that there are no pain receptors is in the brain itself. If a conscious person's brain were exposed, you could stick pins and needles into it and the person would feel no pain. When neurosurgeons perform delicate operations on patients' brains, where it's important to make sure they're not cutting any vital wires as they do the operation, they will usually keep the patient awake during the operation so that he can tell them if he feels any weakness or numbness anywhere as they work on his brain.

Pain is a great motivator. We will do just about anything to avoid the perception of pain. During wartime, the threat of pain to captured enemy troops can usually get them to tell secrets that they would otherwise never reveal. But what is it about pain that makes it "hurt"? After all, the brain is what evaluates pain signals, and all the brain receives to evaluate these pain signals is electric impulses from the pain receptors. These electric impulses traveling along the wires of the brain don't actually hurt inside the brain. So how does the brain make us "feel" the pain? The answer is that since the brain codes everything we experience in the form of electrical impulses, it also codes pain as an electric impulse as well, and like everything else we are consciously aware of, when an electric impulse travels along a unique wire that, when activated, makes us aware of pain, the perception of that pain becomes active anytime an electric impulse travels along that specific wire. The brain could just as easily have coded an electrical impulse traveling on that wire as a pleasant sensation instead of a feeling of pain, but that wouldn't have helped much to get us to correct whatever it was that was damaging our body. The unpleasant sensation of pain from electrical impulses traveling on those wires is almost certainly the result of an evolutionary trial and error mechanism by the brain over millions of years before finally arriving at just the right sensation of unpleasantness that would stimulate a person to pay attention to the pain perception and immediately try to stop it. So, what it is that makes pain "hurt" is just an electric impulse traveling along a special wire in the brain that has been coded by the brain in such a way that whenever it has an electric current traveling along it, it makes a person aware of a sensation of pain.

BEHAVIOR

Behavior is simply the way a person responds to perceptions received through his five senses. When a person perceives a new experience, that perception is converted to an electrical impulse that travels to the brain. It is then compared to similar memories of previous perceptions so that he can respond in the most appropriate manner dictated by previous responses he's made to similar perceptions in the past. The responses that result from all this make up his behavior. Everyone's behavior is necessarily different because everyone has different memories that they compare new perceptions to in order to effect what they consider an appropriate response. For instance, if you and I are walking along and we both see a wasp, I might run for the nearest shelter while you might continue walking. When you observe me running away, you might think my behavior is rather odd or cowardly. After the wasp is gone, I come back out to join you in continuing our walk, and I mention that the last time a wasp stung me, I went into anaphylactic shock and nearly died. You then understand my behavior and no longer think it was odd or cowardly.

Behavior is absolutely and completely subjective. How I perceive your behavior is different from how you perceive your behavior, and how you perceive my behavior is different from how I perceive my behavior. The behavior that someone exhibits is the most appropriate behavior for him in his own frame of reference. In fact, as we've already seen, it is impossible for anyone to respond to a perception in any way *except* what his brain has concluded is the most appropriate way, after analyzing the situation by comparing the new perception to past memories of similar perceptions. If you see someone walking down the road who occasionally hops on one foot, then hops on the other foot, then screams as loud as he can, then crawls on the ground, you will certainly think that his behavior is inappropriate, to say the least. However, to the person exhibiting this behavior, he is responding in the most appropriate manner to new perceptions or conceptions as dictated by his own brain. The brain always chooses the response it feels is the most appropriate for the situation. Everything you see him doing is exactly what his brain is choosing as the most appropriate behavior at that particular time. Even if he's aware that his behavior appears abnormal to others, the fact that he is acting that way means that his brain has decided that by acting that way, he is behaving in the most appropriate manner for whatever the perception or conception was that triggered his acting that way. If I see someone acting strange, I may say that he's just doing it for attention, and I could very well be correct. But for the person acting that way, his brain chose that attention-seeking behavior because, using the new perceptions his brain is receiving, along with the stored memories for comparison, that was decided by his brain to be the most appropriate response for the situation, even if everyone else thought it was the most inappropriate response. A person always chooses the behavior that his brain thinks will derive the most beneficial outcome for himself. The person observing the behavior of another person cannot make any conclusions about the behavior he is witnessing except what his own brain dictates should be the most appropriate response, given the information his brain has from the new perception of the observed behavior and his memories of previous similar perceptions. That is, the observer can only judge the behavior he is seeing by what his own brain has stored in its own memories. This leads to our next topic, judgment.

JUDGMENT

"Judge not lest ye be judged." This sounds like good advice, but unfortunately, it is impossible to follow. We have no choice but to judge everyone and everything because of the way our brain deals with new perceptions.

Judgment is the act of comparing a new perception to memories of previous similar perceptions and conceptions so that the most appropriate response can be made. What occurred previously is used to determine how one should respond now. While behavior refers to the physical response a person makes after an analysis of new perceptions takes place in the brain, judgment refers to the actual process of analyzing the new perceptions in the brain.

When we perceive an event, it gets stored in our memory banks for future reference. When we perceive the same or similar event again, we will call upon our stored memories to see what happened the last time that type of event occurred, so that we can respond in an appropriate manner to this new, similar event. The act of storing the previous perception in our memory bank sets the stage for judgment to occur. For instance, let's say I take a walk every evening after work. During the course of my walks, I meet different people along the way, and I usually smile and bid them a good day. During one particular walk, I meet a man with several tattoos on his body who pulls out a gun and robs me. What do you think will happen the next time I happen to be out walking and I see a man approaching who also has several tattoos? My brain will compare this perception to previous similar perceptions and choose a response that will be equivalent to thinking, "Watch out for this man approaching because he is going to try to rob me." Although it may turn out that the man is a perfectly wonderful person who just happens to like tattoos, I have no choice but to make a judgment about him based on my past experiences of similar situations. That is simply the way the brain is set up to deal with perceptions and it is not going to change unless new perceptions are experienced that gradually change it. For instance, if I begin meeting several people during my daily walks who have tattoos, and none of them try to rob me, after awhile I will no longer associate seeing tattoos on people with their robbing me. In this case, the new perceptions of not being robbed are stored in my memory and may gradually replace the stored memory of my getting robbed by a man with tattoos. It is like a stimulus – response situation. The brain perceives a stimulus, and then responds in the most appropriate manner, based on what worked as a response to that type stimulus in the past.

ARTIFICIAL INTELLIGENCE

With the progress in making computers smaller and more powerful, many scientists feel that some day we will be able to duplicate the function of the human brain using computer technology. This field is referred to as "artificial intelligence" (AI). We will discuss some of the problems that confront those who seek AI.

One of the main differences between a brain and a computer is the speed of electric impulses, which may allow more integration at slower speeds, as occurs in the brain. Electric signals in a computer travel at approximately the speed of light, while electric impulses in the brain travel at about fifty to one hundred miles per hour – considerably slower. If the electric impulses traveled as fast in the brain as they do in a computer, any activity that occurred in any part of the brain would activate every wire that makes up the brain, since they are all connected either directly or indirectly. This would result in constant seizure activity in the brain. (A seizure is an excessive amount of electrical activity in the brain that can spread from one small area to the entire neocortex.) However, since the electric impulses travel so slow in the brain, relative to a computer, they can't spread everywhere before the next impulse arrives for evaluation, canceling out the previous one. In this case, faster does not equal better.

Brains are much more adaptable than machines. Word meanings change over time in human language, as do concepts, and the same word can mean different things depending on how a person uses it. The memories in AI are unchanging in the meanings of the language programmed into them. AI can't conceptualize like a human brain either.

While the brain uses neurotransmitters to connect each wire to another so that the strength of the connections can be adjusted more widely by changing the amount of neurotransmitter released at the terminal end of the wire, the connections of wires in a computer are not able to be adjusted to increase or decrease the strength of the connection as they receive more electric impulses. The brain also grows more nerve endings to connect to others as needed to suit its needs but AI cannot add more wires as it needs them.

AI can't understand the context of interaction with another person, but because the brain constantly updates its memories as new perceptions are received, it is relatively easy for the brain to understand context. For instance, people don't always say what they really are thinking, and you have to rely on body language and changes in speech inflection to determine what they really mean. AI does not have the capacity to do this. Emotion also plays a big part in the functioning of the human brain. AI could possibly be programmed for stronger connections to satisfy the emotional component, but when emotions change in the brain with new perceptions and time, AI would not be able to do the same.

We store "situations" in the form of related memories about perceptions in our brains, rather than just words or numbers. AI stores individual facts, which would make it nearly impossible to recall all the correct facts to put together a situation just as it occurred. Brains also have the ability to draw from several memory systems at one time, in parallel, while AI would have to draw from one memory before proceeding to the next memory, in series. There has been some progress in this area with AI, using quantum principles to draw from several memories at the same time, but it is still in its infancy.

SUMMARY

In this chapter, the main point being conveyed is that the brain itself is ultimately what determines everything, including what exists, what is right and wrong, how all experience (perception) is to be interpreted, and what actions need to be performed to further the brain's only interest, which is itself.

WHO ARE WE, REALLY?

CHOICE

In this chapter, we will discuss how we make decisions, what guides we use in decision-making, which types of people make which types of decisions, how our decisions are influenced by our value of human life, and the consequences of our decisions. But first, we will need to discuss whether we even have a free will for making decisions.

FREE WILL VS. PRE-DESTINY

Pre-destiny is centered on the premise that in classical physics, everything is pre-determined by prior occurrences. Nothing happens randomly. Instead, every action is the result of some previous action. If you believe that everything that occurs in the future can be accurately predicted via physics, chemistry, and math calculations, then there should be no free will, because everything happens as a cause and effect of what occurred before it. That is, all future events can be calculated in advance if the initial motion of all of the atoms at the beginning of time were known. One could simply apply the laws of physics to the movement of those atoms and extrapolate where they would be sometime in the future or, working backwards, sometime in the past. Knowing this, one could then predict, for example, where you would be standing at a certain time in a certain future year. Ultimately, pre-destiny should depend on whether one believes that the submicroscopic energy fields that make up all matter move around on a predetermined path or not.

If pre-destiny is an accurate description of the way things are, then this implies there is no free will. If there's no free will, then we are not responsible for anything we do because we have no choice but to do exactly what pre-determined calculations predict we must do. Taking this one step further, we can say that if pre-destiny is the way things are, then we really aren't any different than rocks in the overall scheme of things. That is, we can accurately predict what a rock will do without any surprises, and with pre-destiny, we could accurately predict what a human being will do without any surprises.

In order for us to be able to discuss anything further about free will, or free choice, we must either show that pre-destiny can't exist, or that if it can exist, it can't interfere with our freedom to choose. First we'll show that pre-destiny can't exist, and then we'll show that even if it could exist, it still couldn't affect our freedom to choose.

You may recall from the physics chapter in Part I that matter is dynamic. It is constantly being eliminated from our universe in black holes and it is constantly being created out of nothing to replace what is lost in black holes. When matter is eliminated in a black hole, it is lost forever and no longer exists. Therefore it can no longer be subject to the predictions of math and physics calculations. Likewise, there is no way math and physics calculations can predict when and where matter will suddenly pop into our universe out of nothing. These two facts prove quite simply that it is impossible to predict from previous events what must happen in the future or what must have happened in the past. Even though we could possibly calculate when certain atoms would enter black holes and disappear from existence, there would be no way to predict anything about those atoms after they disappear in the black hole, or calculate when and where matter would pop into existence to replace that lost matter. The key to disproving that pre-destiny is a product of accurate calculations about what will happen in the future is that once matter disappears from existence, it is no longer subject to being used in calculations, and if it can no longer be used in calculations, then no predictions about where it will be and what it will be doing at some time in the future, or in the past, can be made. It is as simple as that.

Now let's show that even if pre-destiny could exist, it couldn't affect free will. In order for me to have free will, or free choice, there must be two or more options for me in a particular situation, and I must not be "forced" to choose any particular one. The key word here is "forced." If it could be calculated ahead of time which choice I was going to make, but I was not aware of the choice the calculations predicted I would make, nor was I being "forced" to choose the option predicted by the calculations, then the calculations of what my choice would be have absolutely nothing to do with the choice I actually make. To make this more clear, we'll use an example of an ancient philosopher named Zeno, who was known for his famous paradoxes. The most famous of the Zeno paradoxes concerns Achilles and the turtle. If Achilles can run ten times faster than the turtle, and the turtle has a ten-yard lead at the outset, then when Achilles has run ten yards to catch up to the turtle, the turtle has moved ahead one yard. When Achilles runs this yard, the slow turtle has moved on one tenth of a yard. Each time Achilles reaches the position where the turtle had been, the turtle has moved on some small distance, so that Achilles will never catch up even though he moves so much faster. The problem with the logic in the conclusions of this paradox is that it assumes that what the turtle does affects what Achilles does, and it should be obvious that this is not the case. Achilles will pass the turtle before the turtle has gone two yards because Achilles' movement is not affected by the turtle's movement. They are "mutually exclusive" events. The same principle applies to pre-destiny. The fact that one could theoretically calculate exactly where every atom in the universe is at the present time, then predict, based on the principles of math and physics, where all those atoms will be at some time in the future cannot possibly have any effect on someone making a choice in the future. They are mutually exclusive events, which means that neither of them affects the other. For example, suppose someone calculated that I would be standing in a donut shop at a specific time one year from now, trying to decide whether to buy a chocolate or maple glazed donut, and that I was going to choose the chocolate donut. Would those calculations "force" me to choose the chocolate donut? They would not, because the calculations of my choice and the actual choice I made are mutually exclusive events. If I knew ahead of time what the calculations showed, that wouldn't prevent me from picking the maple donut. Because the calculations and my choosing are mutually exclusive events, the calculations can only predict as long as they don't cross over into the realm of my choosing – that is, as long as I'm not *aware* of what the calculations predict. If I become aware of what the calculations predict for me at some time in the future, then the calculations immediately become dependent upon my choice. I can then choose in such a way to prove them wrong because at that point, my choosing and the calculations that predict my choice are no longer mutually exclusive, meaning that what I do now affects what the calculations predict, ultimately changing the calculations. The predictions of the calculations are only valid as long as they aren't known by the person doing the choosing. If the calculated predictions are known at the time a choice is being made, the calculated predictions necessarily break down because they become dependent upon the choice being made rather than remaining independent of it. (If this seems strange to you, remember the famous "double-slit" experiment from the section on quantum physics in chapter 4, which shows by experiment that we can, and do, change the outcome of an event just by the act of observing it.) Therefore, even if it were possible to calculate where all the atoms in the universe would be at a certain time, allowing one to predict the future, those calculations would only be accurate as long as no one knew what they predicted before making a choice. In other words, those calculations could only predict the future as long as we weren't aware of them. Once we become aware of them, they can no longer predict what choices we will make because they lose their mutual exclusiveness from our choosing. The result is that they cannot possibly affect any choices we make. Free will would still have to exist.

How does free will work? As with most of the other processes we've discussed, free will is a process relegated to the brain. It consists of receiving perceptions in the brain via the five senses, comparing those perceptions to stored memories of similar perceptions or conceptions, then choosing the best response to make, based on the analysis. It is important to remember that the response chosen will always be the one that either directly or indirectly has the most benefit for the person making the response, as the brain can only know itself and can only choose what benefits itself the most. It may appear superficially that a choice being made will benefit another at the expense of the person making the choice, but this is never the actual case. For instance, making the choice that seems to benefit another more than the choice-maker more than likely contains an emotional component that would haunt the choice-maker if he didn't make the choice that appears superficially to benefit another more than himself.

THE VALUE OF LIFE

How much is a human life worth? We choose the answer for this question on a daily basis, and the answer rarely seems consistent. When trying to get the automakers to put more safety devices in cars, at costs in the hundreds of millions of dollars, we often hear people say that "if it saves just one life, it's worth the cost," the implication being that human life is more valuable than money. If this were true, then we should be willing to spend all the money we have to save even one person from dying in a car wreck. We don't do this, and we don't demand that automakers put the most expensive safety devices in cars, because that would make cars much more expensive to buy. This implies that there must be some dollar value we do attach to a human life. When a bum lying on a sidewalk on skid row dies, he may lie there for several hours before someone finally calls the police to have him picked up and taken to the morgue. But if the president of the United States died, all the television and radio stations would announce it, dignitaries from other countries would send condolences, and the nation would mourn his death. If one of the members of my immediate family died, it would have a much more profound affect on me than if a neighbor I didn't know very well died. So, not only do we put a dollar value on human life, but it appears that we also choose to value some lives more than others.

We each choose the value of any particular life exclusively by how that life affects us personally, either directly or indirectly. That is the only possible way we can choose because every choice we make is relative to our personal frame of reference and depends on an analysis of the stored memories in our brain, and our brain only. If I read in the obituary section of the newspaper that someone I've never heard of died recently, there is no possible way I can activate any memories of previous perceptions about that person in my brain because I don't have any, and that means I can't make a choice about a response to the specific perception of reading the person's name in the newspaper. I would not make a choice regarding the value of that person's life, but would read his obituary, just as I would any other article in the newspaper, and then move on to the next article. However, if I read an obituary in the newspaper relating to a person that I knew very well, I would have stored memories in my brain relating to that person, and would then be able to analyze this new perception of the person's death, using those stored memories of him, and would probably make some kind of a response, such as feeling sad, making preparations to attend the funeral, or calling the family to express my condolences.

Television commercials often show starving children in impoverished countries in order to appeal to the emotional memory areas of our brain. The spokesperson then asks for donations to help feed these people. Most of us feel sympathy for the people shown in these commercials, but only a few of us actually choose to send money to help feed them. The reason is because these starving people don't affect us either directly or indirectly, since our brain usually doesn't have any emotional memories formed from previous perceptions (experiences) relating to them. Once the commercial is over, we immediately forget about what we just saw, since it doesn't really affect us, and get ready to receive more new perceptions from the television via our sense of vision and hearing. But what about the people who do send donations to help feed these starving people after hearing about their plight in the commercial? Even though they don't have any previous experiences with starving people, they do have emotional memories related to helping those in need, and that's what causes their brain to choose to send money to help feed the starving people. Their emotional memories of helping those in need may have originated from the teachings of their parents as they grew up, from the teaching they receive if they attend weekly religious services, and so on. The compulsion to donate money is directly related to the strength of the emotional memories in the brains of the people who watch the commercial on television. Those people with the strongest emotional memories about starving people will be more likely to choose to donate money to their cause.

Our own life is important to us, but self-preservation is not the most important thing to our brain. This may sound strange since it's been mentioned so often that our brain can only know itself in its own frame of reference, and therefore always makes the choice that benefits itself the most. It would seem to follow that the most logical choice, then, would be for our brain to choose what preserves our own life over any other possible outcome. The reason this seemingly most logical choice is not necessarily accurate is because of those pesky strong emotional memories that each of us has stored in our brain. Remember that for most people in our society, emotional memories usually dictate choosing a response that is the most fair, while logical memories are more concerned with choosing a response that benefits us the most without regard for anyone else. The emotional memories can be so strong that when they cause us to make the fairest choice that truly benefits ourselves the most, instead of the logical choice that would only seem to benefit ourselves the most, that choice is more likely to lead to our demise. For instance, suppose a man is driving along an abandoned street late at night and sees another man attacking a woman on the side of the road. His brain analyzes this situation and because the man has very strong emotional memories for fairness, either because he was taught this over and over as he grew up, or because of some other reason, he stops his car and comes to the aid of the woman. Logically, his decision to stop and help makes no sense because he is much more likely to meet his demise by helping, especially if the attacker has a weapon, than by driving on without stopping. So he puts his life at risk for someone he does not even know because he has some strong emotional memories in his brain that dictate he should choose the course of action that is the most fair. Suppose he chooses the response dictated by the logical memories in his brain, even though the emotional memories don't agree. He will continue to receive electric impulses from the strong

253

emotional memories in the response area of the brain long after the choice has been made not to stop and help the woman. This results in strong emotional feelings of guilt and shame that can last his entire life, since emotionally dictated response impulses continue to be sent to the response area of the brain until they are heeded. So the best choice is not the one that preserves the choice-maker's life, but the one that the analysis of the situation by the brain dictates will allow the choice-maker to feel that he made the correct decision, based on all the memories he has stored in his brain that are related to similar situations. In other words, in this case, "peace of mind" is more important than life.

Someone might argue that it doesn't make any sense for the brain to choose a course of action that is more likely to cause the demise of that brain (and the body it belongs to), especially since we are products of evolution. From an evolutionary standpoint, this looks like a case of evolution in reverse. That is, if some emotions can cause us to make choices that are more likely to cause our demise, then the development of those emotions seems to be a step backward on the evolutionary tree, and those emotions are more likely to lead to the eventual downfall of mankind. We take care of the poor, the sick, and the elderly instead of letting them die; we feed those who are starving, even though we know that doing so will likely make them healthy enough to reproduce, creating more starving people, taxing our very limited resources even more; and we do all this because of certain emotional memories stored in our brain. The answer to this seeming paradox is found in the fact that evolution is the result of mutations in our genetic material. When a good mutation occurs that makes us more adaptable to our environment, it is more likely to be passed on to following generations. When a bad mutation occurs that makes us less adaptable to our environment, it is less likely to be passed on to future generations and usually ends up being eliminated from the population fairly quickly. But what about those mutations that are just "sort of" bad? They may ultimately be bad for our eventual survival, but may not be bad enough that they are eliminated quickly from our genetic material. It is those mutations that are responsible for things like emotions of compassion, which are not beneficial for the ultimate survival of mankind, but are not bad enough that they end up being eliminated right away. One of the errors that social scientists seem to be prone to making about evolution is assuming that every genetic change always leads to better-adapted organisms. For instance, if a certain trait is exhibited by a human being, it is assumed that it must have a positive evolutionary survival benefit or it wouldn't exist. This is the wrong way to look at it because it assumes that we are at the final stage of evolution where all the "bugs" have been worked out. However, this is not the case. Right now, we probably have hundreds of mutations in our genetic makeup that will need to be eliminated eventually if our species is ultimately to survive. Evolution is an ongoing process and sometimes we develop bad mutations that aren't immediately eliminated. In fact, over hundreds of thousands of years, these mutations can be incorporated into all human beings without causing the demise of the species. Over millions of years, though, they may have to be eliminated through the process of natural selection in order for the species to survive. The development and manifestation of certain emotions seems to fit with these types of mutations. One of the reasons these certain emotions have not been eliminated from our species, even though they have a negative effect on our eventual survival, is because they seem to be self-perpetuating. Their very existence in our brain causes our brain to choose these emotions as a positive rather than a negative entity. For instance, someone who is more logical and less emotional is generally not looked upon by others as being a desirable mate. We prefer a mate who is more capable of displaying the emotion of compassion, for example, to a mate who is more logical and unfeeling. So the more logical person is less likely to produce offspring that resemble him genetically in being more logical and less compassionate. This odd phenomenon can cause certain emotions to be a part of our species for a much longer time. Eventually, though, these types of emotions that seem to deal with things like compassion will either be eliminated or severely reduced as part of our genetic make-up because if they aren't, the compassion most of us have for less fortunate people may cause the extinction of all humans. A billion years from now, people may look back at us through recorded history and shake their heads in disbelief at how crude we were with our emotions, just as we look back at ancient man and shake our heads in disbelief at how crude he was without a sophisticated language like we have.

GRATIFICATION

When we make a choice after analyzing a situation, we always choose the option that benefits our self the most. We've already seen that the choice that benefits us the most is not necessarily the one that is most likely to allow our survival, but the one that gives us the most satisfaction, or gratification. We will now look at how we obtain gratification

Because of the way the brain is arranged for making decisions, there are two ways to evaluate a situation and respond to it. We can respond in such a way that we get immediate gratification, or we can respond in such a way that the gratification is deferred until later. These two types of responses are so distinctly formed in our brain that all people can be divided into two separate groups based on their method of obtaining gratification. There are those who usually seek immediate gratification and those who usually seek deferred gratification.

What happens in the brain of someone who has a tendency to seek immediate gratification is that perceptions are received by one or more of the five senses, then an electrical impulse is transmitted from those receptors to the brain, where the memories of similar perceptions are compared to the incoming perceptions to effect the appropriate response, based on previous responses to similar perceptions, and that response is carried out to obtain the most gratification right then. However, for someone who has a tendency to seek deferred gratification, when the new, incoming perceptions are compared to memories of similar perceptions in the brain, they also cause memories of conceptions to be activated, as well as the formation of new conceptions from combining various similar memories of perceptions and conceptions. This results in new ideas or plans that the brain conceives will result in more gratification later if certain responses that are less gratifying are made now. For example, I know a man who is a building contractor. He had a carpenter working for him who was putting up walls on an office building. The contractor needed three rooms to be finished in three days, so he told the carpenter that he would give him an extra five hundred dollars if he could finish those three rooms in three days. The carpenter laughed at him and said there was no possible way to do those three rooms in three days. After thinking over the situation, the contractor went back to the carpenter and told him he would give him a case of beer at the end of that day if he could finish one of the rooms. The carpenter worked a little faster that day and finished the first room that day. He received his case of beer at the end of the day. The next day, the contractor told the carpenter he'd give him another case of beer if could finish the second room by the end of that day. The carpenter completed the second room that day and received his second case of beer that afternoon. The third day, the contractor told the carpenter he'd give him another case of beer if could finish the third room by the end of that day. The carpenter completed the third room that day and received his third case of beer that afternoon. The contractor got the three rooms finished in three days, just like he wanted, and instead of having to pay out a bonus of five hundred dollars at the end of the third day, he only had to buy three cases of beer instead. Someone might wonder why the carpenter was willing to do the same amount of work over three days for three cases of beer instead of the much larger bonus of five hundred dollars. In this admittedly extreme (but true) case, the carpenter did not have the capacity to conceptualize in his brain to seek the greatest gratification, or reward, by delaying it. When the perceptions of the contractor's proposition reached the carpenter's brain, the only thing he could compare them to were previous memories of perceptions which only included doing one room at a time because that was what he had stored in his memories as the amount of work he could do in one day. He did not have the capacity to conceptualize how much work he could do in three days. Typically, children younger than the teenage years are not able to conceptualize like an adult. That's why they are unlikely to exhibit anything but immediate gratification. When a parent tells a child to perform some chore now in order to attend a carnival in two weeks, the parent shouldn't be surprised when this doesn't work. When there is no immediate gratification for the child, he can't conceptualize in his brain that he is receiving a reward later for the chore he is doing now.

Seeking long-term goals is equivalent to deferred gratification. People who go to college with a final purpose in mind, or people who open a new business, are practicing deferred gratification. When they receive new perceptions in their brains for analysis, they are able to conceptualize these new perceptions with memories of similar perceptions to come up with a plan that involves making a series of responses over time that don't individually provide the most satisfaction at that particular time, but that allow the final response sometime in the future to give them a much greater gratification.

We occasionally hear of a plan to live life "one day at a time." This plan is usually proposed when someone has had a setback in life. For instance, alcoholics are told in Alcoholics Anonymous meetings to work on abstaining from alcohol one day at a time. People who have lost their jobs and are having difficulty getting back to their prior level of functioning are advised to take one day at a time. Why does this choice work? The reason is because choosing to abolish long-range goals allows one to act in a more concrete manner instead of conceptualizing, or planning ahead. Once an alcoholic starts thinking about abstaining from alcohol for the next several years instead of just until the next day, he will be more likely to conceptualize the difficulty in abstaining for so long and go right back to drinking. This is similar to the carpenter who couldn't imagine building three rooms in three days, but could build one room a day for three days. Planning to "live one day at a time" is much more likely to work for someone whose brain usually seeks immediate gratification than for someone whose brain is more geared to practicing deferred gratification because those who seek immediate gratification are less prone to conceptualizing situations for long term gratification anyway.

CONSEQUENCES OF DECISIONS

It's been mentioned several times that we always choose the response to a situation that benefits ourselves the most, but just what are the results, or consequences, of those decisions we think are benefiting us the most? For instance, what happens when we make a mistake and the decision we choose has no benefit for us? First of all, mistakes almost never occur within the brain itself. Our brain receives input from our five senses. Once that input arrives in the brain, it is automatically compared to previous memories of similar input and the best response is made based on the results of the analysis. The final response is always the best one resulting from the analysis of the information about the situation. Of course, sometimes our senses are fooled by things such as optical illusions, echoes, and so on. And sometimes when we respond to perceptions, we don't have an adequate fund of knowledge to make the correct response. But these are not really mistakes, per se. They are due to erroneous input or inadequate memories, respectively. Mistakes in processing would be extremely rare within a healthy brain because of the way memories are stored on the wires that make up the brain. They are only activated by an impulse that matches them. If someone asked me what six times nine equals, and I say that it equals fifty-six, there are two possible reasons for this "mistake." Either I don't have an adequate fund of knowledge to recall or compute that the correct answer is fifty-four, or I have responded to the question before my brain's analysis of the problem was complete, in which case I might quickly follow my wrong answer by saying, "Oh, I mean fifty-four."

Some people tend to make decisions that result in the least amount of change, having neither a very good nor a very bad possible outcome, while others make decisions such that the result will either be very good or very bad. For instance, two golfers are getting ready to tee off on a short hole. There is a huge lake in front of the green. The first golfer elects to hit short of the lake and play it safe, knowing he will be fairly sure of getting a four on the hole. The second golfer decides to go for the green, knowing that if he hits it, he will almost certainly get a three on the hole, but that if he misses it, he will probably get a five or a six. Each golfer chooses his particular method of playing the hole because of how his brain functions, including the types of stored memories his brain contains, the concentrations of the various neurotransmitters in his brain, and so on. Is one golfer's method of playing the hole any more correct than the other golfer's? The answer is that it isn't. Whatever each golfer's brain dictates as the correct way for him to play the hole is the best way he can play the hole, since the brain always compares new perceptions to memories of similar perceptions and conceptions and chooses its best response.

No one makes a choice about anything that doesn't affect him in either a direct or indirect way. When perceptions reach the brain that don't affect the person who is analyzing them, they are simply ignored. No response is made by the brain, no memories are made of the perceptions, and within a few minutes, when new perceptions enter the brain and replace them, the person will no longer be aware that those perceptions were ever even evaluated. For instance, we have seen famous people on television speaking out for doing more research on various illnesses, such as spinal cord injuries, Parkinson's disease, and post-partum depression. Until these people became intimately associated with these problems themselves by becoming afflicted with them, they would probably not have cared whether research was being done in those particular fields or not. Although some may say that this is just selfishness, it is really just the brain doing what it is programmed to do. The brain pays attention to perceptions that affect it and disregards perceptions that don't affect it.

What is the most important factor a person considers when making any choice? The first inclination would be to answer that survival is the most important. This would be wrong, though, as mentioned earlier in this chapter. All one has to do is visit a nursing home and talk with the residents there to find out that survival is not very high on the list of priorities when making choices. We could also consider power, money, popularity, and a host of other factors a person considers as primary in decision-making, but examples to prove that these are not correct are also abundant. The most important factor that anyone considers when making a choice is contentment. "Peace of mind" is another term that means essentially the same thing as contentment. The reason why contentment is the most important factor considered when making a choice is because the brain is the source of making choices in the first place, and it strives to create its environment so that there is just the right amount of electrical activity going on within it. It doesn't want to have to make "fight or flight" responses if it can avoid them, it doesn't want to analyze an excessive amount of incoming information, and it doesn't want to deal with emotions if it can avoid this, because emotions require more attention during analysis and they cause the release of lots of other chemicals around the body and brain for various reasons. The brain prefers to have just enough background electrical activity to be able to day-dream, to know when it needs to be fed, when it needs to sleep, and so on.

SUMMARY

By showing that pre-destiny cannot exist, and that even if it did, it could not affect our ability to make choices, we've established that free will does exist. It has also been shown that the value of human life changes depending on the frame of reference of who is doing the deciding.

When making decisions about being rewarded for actions, some people make choices that allow immediate gratification and others make choices that allow for delayed gratification that they conceive will be larger.

We make decisions in such a way that the consequences of those decisions will be what the memories stored in our brain predict will give us the greatest contentment.

WHO ARE WE, REALLY?

MORALS AND ETHICS

Most of the information that has been discussed to this point has shown that individuals usually make the final determination of the way things are. In this chapter, we will see that morals and ethics are not only determined by the person who is making a response, but also by the observers of that response – society. This is because morals and ethics are products of a society, not of single individuals.

Morality usually refers to a process that occurs within the brain itself, while ethics refers to the actions a person performs in response to what his morality dictates. Morals and ethics can only exist within human societies because they require the formation of concepts in the brain, and only humans have demonstrated an ability to conceptualize. They consist of standards on how people within a society should interact with each other. Anyone living in a particular society must adhere to these standards in order to be judged as a member in good moral and ethical standing within that society. The purpose of the moral and ethical rules of society is to provide a standard whereby everyone in that society can live together in harmony without any member having to worry that someone will take unfair advantage of him. This is the definition of the standard rules of society. That is, an act can only be considered moral or immoral if it has something to do with people living together in harmony in a society without any member taking unfair advantage of any other member. If a society had no moral or ethical standards, everyone would be free to do whatever he wanted to whomever he wanted whenever he wanted. A functional society could not exist in this case. It would be a situation of "every man for himself," or a "state of nature."

What constitutes a society? A society is the highest order of a group of people living under the same universally recognized governing body for the sole purpose of facilitating living together in harmony without anyone taking unfair advantage of anyone else. For instance, religious groups in America don't constitute societies because each of the members of the various religious groups are also citizens of the United States, which is a higher order of members living under the same governing body. In addition, the purpose of religious groups is not for allowing the members to live together in harmony without anyone taking unfair advantage of anyone else. Their purpose is for dealing with issues related to spiritual life. A society can be very large, composed of over a billion people, like the Republic of China, or it can be very small, composed of less than fifty people, like some of the bush tribes of Africa.

NATURE VS. NURTURE

What are morals? We've already mentioned that matters of morality take place in the brain, so we know that morality has to have something to do with the wires of the brain, since that's what makes up the entire brain. We also know from experience that a person's morality doesn't change whimsically, so this means morality must be stored in some particular way in the brain and it must be fairly unchanging, or rigid. The only way this can occur is if morality is stored as something permanent. So now we've determined that morality consists of something stored fairly permanently in the brain, but we haven't shown whether this stored material is there as part of the coded genetic framework of the brain when it is developing in utero or if it is stored as one experiences life.

For at least a few thousand years, there has been an ongoing debate about the origin of morality. Some people believe that morals are inherent and coded in our genetic material while others believe that morality develops as a learning process during life experiences through perceptions, which are then formed into permanent memories in the brain. Still others take a middle-of-the-road approach in believing that some of morality is encoded in our genetic material while the rest is the result of life experiences, or perceptions.

The investigations into the makeup of the human genome have shown that it is physically impossible to have genetic codes for anything but a basic framework for the wiring of the brain upon which memories will be formed as a person experiences perceptions during his lifetime. In other words, if the genetic code were responsible for coding such things as individual memories about morality inherited from one's parents, there would necessarily have to be much more genetic material than we are known to have. This fact alone would be enough to prove that morality results solely from environmental experience (perceptions) rather than being the product of inheritance.

One of the reasons that it may seem like morality is inherited is because a person is the most receptive to forming new memories when he is a child, and the people who are the most influential over a child during these peak memory-forming years are his parents. (You may recall from a previous chapter that children have a much larger number of wires in the brain for development with memories than adults do.) It would stand to reason then that a child is more likely to form memories dealing with morality that are very closely aligned with those of his parents.

If morality were inherited instead of learned, then it should not differ from one society to another. The fact that morality does differ in different societies would imply that it is environmental, or learned. For instance, in some societies it is considered immoral for women to appear in public with any part of their skin exposed, while in other societies, neither men nor women wear any clothing at all and this is not considered immoral in those societies. To say that morality is inherited, given that it is obviously different from one society to another, would be somewhat akin to surgically removing the tails from a particular breed of dog for several generations, then expecting them to begin being born without tails. In other words, you can't change a genetic trait by modifying what it codes for. You can only change a genetic trait by modifying the genes themselves. Since morality and ethics are different in different societies, they have to be something that is a product of the various societies rather than a product of genetic makeup.

What if a person were stranded all alone on a deserted island? Would morals and ethics exist on that island? In this case, it would depend on whether that lone person living on the island had ever been a member of a society. If he had been a member of a society before he became stranded on the deserted island, then he would have memories of perceptions that dealt with the standard morals and ethics of that society, and any responses he made to new perceptions on the deserted island would entail recalling memories of similar perceptions for comparison, and these would necessarily include memories dealing with morals and ethics. If he were lost at sea as a baby, washed ashore on the deserted island, and was then raised by animals on the island, he would never have been exposed to perceptions of standard morals and ethics of a society, so he would have no memories dealing with morals and ethics. He could not be moral or immoral, nor could he perform any ethical or unethical acts because morals and ethics are defined only in societies as standards for allowing people to live together in harmony without taking advantage of each other. Therefore, a requirement for judging himself or being judged by others as moral or immoral is that he be a member of a society. (This will be discussed further in the section on "right" and "wrong.")

How are morals stored in the brain? They are stored just as any other perceptions are stored as permanent memories. They can be stored as emotional memories or as logical memories, but the stronger the memories are that pertain to morality, the more likely they are to have been stored as emotional memories. For instance, suppose a father sees his son outside hitting a dog with a stick. He runs outside and begins yelling at the son to stop because it's wrong to hit the dog. The son forms a memory in his brain of hitting the dog being associated with his father yelling at him, and because his father's yelling also invoked a fear response in the son, the memory will also have the emotional content of fear associated with it and will be stored as a strong emotional response in his brain. So now the son has a strong emotional memory stored in his brain that associates hitting a dog with his father yelling at him to stop. The next time he has a stick in his hand and a dog is nearby, that new perception will trigger the recall of the stored similar perception for comparison and his response will be to not hit the dog. If the father also explained to the son after he yelled at him to stop hitting the dog that it is wrong because it hurts the dog, and then asks the son how he would like it if someone hit him with a stick, the son will also form a logical memory of hitting the dog with a stick being similar to someone hitting him with a stick. He would then recall this logical memory for comparison too when the perception of seeing a dog while holding a stick arose again. The point of this example is to show that morals are not stored as "morals" in the brain, but as simple perceptions and conceptions, just like any other perceptions and conceptions. What makes them moral or immoral is whether they have anything to do with the standard rules of morality dictated by society. If they can be related to the standards of morality dictated by society, then those stored memories can be judged as being moral or immoral when they are used to help formulate a response by the brain after their comparison to new perceptions. For instance, the same response to a new perception by the same person could be interpreted as moral in one society and immoral in another society. The morality of an act or response is entirely due to the "rules" of a society. Since the rules are a product of society, they can't possibly be genetically coded. They must be learned.

Someone might argue that it may be true that society makes the rules, or determines what is moral and immoral, but society is made up of members and the members of society must use their brains to determine these rules, so in the end it is brains that make the rules about morality. And if it is ultimately brains that make the rules about morality, then this means the rules could still be coded genetically. The answer to this argument is the same as stated earlier – the genetic code is simply not large enough to code for specific moral memories. It could only code for the general framework of the brain. Any memories that are carried on this framework must only come from life experiences, or learning. So the rules of any society, which ultimately come from brains, are simply memories of various perceptions, or experiences. If these memories happen to have anything to do with either benefiting or harming members of that society, then, by definition, they are memories that deal with morality.

What happens when someone who was fairly immoral throughout his life suddenly decides to change and begins acting in such a way that the society he is a part of judges his actions now as being moral instead of immoral? In order for a person to change from being immoral to being moral, a person must change his permanent memories since they are ultimately what his brain uses to determine how he will respond to new perceptions. He can change his permanent memories in a variety of ways and the difficulty with changing them is in proportion to how strong the memories are. Emotionally associated memories will be harder to change than logically associated memories because the emotionally associated memories are more strongly formed in the brain. For instance, suppose I've been an immoral person my entire life, robbing and stealing from people at every opportunity. One night while I'm ransacking someone's house, I'm surprised by the owner of the house whom I thought was gone. He levels a shotgun at me and pulls the trigger, but the gun jams and doesn't fire. I run for the door and escape before he can figure out the problem and try to shoot me again. After I'm safely away from there, it dawns on me that if I don't change my ways, I could end up dead. The perception of the home owner pulling the trigger of the gun pointed at my chest forms a very strong emotional memory in my brain – so strong, in fact, that it can replace the previous permanent memories associated with stealing from people's houses. Whenever I think about entering a person's house to steal, the strong memory of the shotgun pointed at me will be recalled from memory for comparison and it is unlikely that I will respond by wanting to go into a house to steal again. Another example involves people who become "born again" Christians. They usually have become disenchanted with being an outcast in their society because of an immoral lifestyle, as judged by the rules of society, and the memories of this disenchantment are recalled for comparison to new perceptions that previously would have elicited an immoral response. If the memories of the disenchantment are strong enough, they will override the previous memories and the person will become more moral. If morality and ethics were coded genetically, rather than being a product of society, it would be nearly impossible to change from being immoral to being moral, or vice versa.

RIGHT AND WRONG

When discussing "right" and "wrong" in this chapter, we are referring to "morally right" and "morally wrong," because morals (and ethics) only apply to the rules of society, while the terms "right" and "wrong" by themselves can refer to the rules of many subgroups within a society, such as religious groups, private or public companies, sporting events, and many other things.

Are there any absolute standards of "right" and "wrong?" In other words, are there some things that are always wrong, or immoral, in any society, under any circumstances? The answer is that there are not. There is no example of any act that can be determined to be wrong at all times in all societies. For instance, some of the acts one might think would always be considered wrong in any society may include killing, rape, mutilation, and torture. However, there are societies that exist in which these things are not considered wrong in certain circumstances. During wars, it is not considered morally wrong to kill the members of the enemy. In some ancient societies, rape was not considered morally wrong as an appropriate punishment for various indiscretions. There have also been societies that would punish thieves by severing various limbs or torturing them, and this was not considered morally wrong in those societies.

A person is taught from childhood what is right and wrong. He learns this from other members of his society. Within his society, there may be standards indicating that some acts are always wrong, or always right, but those standards don't necessarily apply to all societies, just his. If there were only one society on the planet, and every person was a member of that society, then there might be something approaching absolute standards of right or wrong. There could never actually be an absolute standard of right and wrong though, because if it were absolute, it would have to exist even if there were only one person who ever lived on the planet. Since we've already established that right and wrong, or moral and immoral, only exist within a society, and a society must have at least two members for it to exist, then right and wrong can't exist if only one person ever existed on earth. If that one person decided he wanted to commit suicide, for example, there wouldn't be anything right or wrong about it because there were never any standards established by a society for living together in harmony. The person who is committing suicide is doing so because he receives new perceptions via his five senses that he compares to memories of previous perceptions, and the most appropriate response dictated by this analysis within his brain, in his frame of reference, is to commit suicide. It's neither right nor wrong for him. It's just the response his brain dictates as being the most appropriate one to make after comparing the new perceptions he is experiencing with his stored memories of similar perceptions.

When Einstein developed his theory of relativity, many people wondered if the fact that everything was relative meant that moral standards would now be considered relative to each individual frame of reference too, instead of being absolute in a society. The answer is that moral standards are not relative to each individual in a society. The fact that they are referred to as "standards" within a particular society means that they are what all individuals within the society must use to determine whether an act is right or wrong. A person may individually, in his own frame of reference, think that an action he performs is right, based on his brain's analysis of comparing previous memories of perceptions to new perceptions, then responding to this analysis in the way that benefits him the most, but whether he thinks his action is morally right or not doesn't determine whether it actually *is* morally right. Right and wrong are determined by the standard rules of a particular society, and these standards are what determine whether his action was right or wrong, independent of what his brain thinks. For instance, you can think of the societal standards as a medium that performs the same function as air does in carrying sound waves. Sound moves faster towards you if the sound emitter itself is moving towards you because its movement is relative to air, which is the medium that carries the sound. Conversely, light doesn't use a medium like air to travel through space so its speed is always the same whether it's coming from an object moving towards you or from an object moving away from you. Once there is a medium, or standard, then that becomes the reference point from which all measurements are drawn. In the case of measuring sound, that reference point is the air that sound travels through. In the case of morality, that reference point is the set of rules of that society from which all conclusions about right and wrong are drawn. Individual members of a society act in a way that their brains have determined will benefit them the most, but whether their actions are right or wrong can only be determined by comparing them to the standards of their society, not their own individual frame of reference. I may think that anyone who chops down trees to make paper out of them should be shot, and so, in my frame of reference, my brain determines that what will benefit me the most would be to shoot people who chop down trees because they are ruining my environment. Since the society I live in has standards that say it is wrong to shoot people who chop down trees to make paper out of them, it doesn't matter whether I think it is right or not in my own frame of reference. The standards for my society say it is wrong, so therefore it is wrong for me to do it and I can expect to be punished if I do it anyway. The goal of society is to allow people to live together in harmony without taking unfair advantage of each other, and a standard set of rules for what is right and wrong that everyone must adhere to is necessary to achieve this goal.

The societal standards for right and wrong are not static. They continuously and gradually change over time as new information becomes known. For instance, thirty or forty years ago, it was not considered wrong to administer corporal punishment to children for misbehaving at home, in school, and wherever else misbehaving might occur. Now, however, inflicting pain on children in the way of corporal punishment is considered wrong by the rules of our society, and a member of our society can expect to be punished if he practices this method of behavior modification on children.

How do we know whether something is right or wrong? We begin learning these concepts very early in life via perceptions, usually from our parents teaching us. We perceive things via our five senses, analyze it in our brain by the usual process, and then make a response. If that response is morally wrong, we are scolded. We then form a memory of the scolding we just received for the morally wrong response and the next time a similar perception occurs, we recall the memory of the scolding and then we're less likely to make the same response that earned us the scolding the first time. By this trial and error method, we learn what's right and what's wrong. But now someone might wonder who determined that some specific act was right or wrong in the first place, because we already know that everyone has his own ideas about what should be right and wrong in his own frame of reference. The answer is simply that because the goal of society is for everyone in that society to live together in harmony without anyone taking unfair advantage of anyone else, then any action that allows the members of society to live together in harmony without anyone taking unfair advantage of anyone else is morally right, while any action contrary to this is morally wrong. It is usually not difficult for someone to determine this before acting, or responding to a perception. In those cases where it is not readily apparent whether an action that benefits the person who performs that action might negatively impact other members of society, we use the written laws of our constitution to fall back on for guidance. Conversely, in some cases it is obvious that something is morally wrong because it benefits a few while taking unfair advantage of others, but our constitution allows it. In these cases, it is necessary to change the laws to coincide with what's morally right. For instance, it has been shown conclusively that cigarettes are detrimental to those who smoke them, yet our laws still allow them to be sold, in spite of the fact that it is morally wrong to do so, by definition, because it benefits the cigarette makers at the expense of the people who buy the cigarettes.

Suppose it could be shown that anyone in our society who held his left hand on his head for two minutes once a week would positively influence our society in such a way that we would be more likely to live in harmony and not take advantage of each other, and that anyone who did not hold his left hand on his head for two minutes once a week would negatively influence our society in such a way that we would be less likely to live in harmony and would be more likely to take advantage of each other. Would it be morally right to perform this act? Would it be morally wrong not to perform this act? The answer is that it would be morally right to perform the act and it would be morally wrong not to perform the act. The reason is because right and wrong are solely determined by the effect an act has on society, no matter what the act is. If an act has no impact at all on the members of society, then it cannot be judged as being morally right or wrong.

PHILOSOPHY AND MORALITY

Philosophers have argued for years about whether morality is based on emotion or logic (reasoning). Socrates and Plato defended reasoning, arguing that it could provide true knowledge of moral principles and that all human beings could be guided by this knowledge, enabling them to act upon it. Kant also believed that reasoning could lead us to moral truths. For example, he declared that it was wrong for us to use someone for our own ends, and that it was right to act only according to principles that everyone could follow. Hume believed that an act was moral not because it was reasoned to be moral but because it felt moral to the person performing it. Mill believed that the rules of morality should achieve the greatest good for the greatest number of people, even though particular individuals might be worse off as a result.

Now that we know infinitely more about how the brain works than was known when all these philosophers were alive, it is much easier to explain how morality actually does originate as an intrinsic part of our brain. First of all, morality is not based only on logic (reasoning) or only on emotion. It has components drawn from both. As we have mentioned before, all the memories formed in our brain are the direct or indirect result of perceptions we have experienced through our five senses. If we had none of our five senses, and could therefore not perceive anything, we could not form any memories of any type. Once we perceive things and form memories in our brain, we can expand those memories by integrating them together to form new concepts or ideas, and then store those new concepts as more memories. Then we can combine those new memories of concepts to form even more memories of concepts, and all of this expansion of memories can be the result of just one perception we experienced. When we perceive something and store it as a memory, it can be stored as a logical memory or an emotional memory or a combination of both. Since morality is a product of society, and its purpose is to allow us to live together in harmony in that society without anyone taking unfair advantage of anyone else in that society, then any memories we form in our permanent memory base that relate to interacting with others in our society will have a morality component attached to them, meaning that if a new perception occurs later that has something to do with societal interaction, these memories will likely be recalled from stored memory to active memory for comparison to the new perception in order to form the most appropriate response to the new perception. There is no reason the morality component has to be associated with just emotional or just logical memories. A morality component may be attached to either type. For instance, going back to the example of the child hitting the dog with a stick, when the father yells at the child to stop hitting the dog, the child is frightened by his father's yelling, and so he will form an emotional memory of that perception, and there will be a morality issue attached to this emotional memory since it is considered morally wrong to mistreat an animal in our society. When the father also explained to the child that the reason he shouldn't hit the dog with the stick is because it is painful for the dog, this perception causes a logical permanent memory to be formed in the child's brain, and this logical memory will also have a morality issue attached to it. So from this one event, the child forms both emotional and logical memories of a moral issue that he can recall from stored memory to active memory to determine what action he will take the next time he comes into contact with a dog while holding a stick in his hand.

It was mentioned in the previous chapter that we take care of sick people and feed starving people even though this taxes our very limited resources, and we do all this because of emotional memories stored in our brain. The implication here is that the secondary, or social, emotions of guilt and pride cause us to do this. Now we can add another reason to why we do these things. Our standard rules of society demand it as part of being moral and ethical members. If we did not feed the starving nor take care of the sick, that would be violating the purpose of a society – to live in harmony without anyone taking unfair advantage of anyone else. Not caring for the sick or feeding the hungry would benefit each of us who are not sick or hungry, because it would save our limited resources, but it would be at the expense of those who are sick and hungry, so it violates the standard rules of our society. Anyone who did not take care of the sick and feed the hungry members of our society who are in good standing would be considered immoral by the standard rules of our society.

Can an irrational person be subject to society's rules of morality and ethics? The answer is that everyone living in a particular society is subject to that society's rules of morality and ethics, without exception. Just because someone does not have the capacity to recall memories that deal with morality when he analyzes a new perception in his brain and then responds to it, that does not entitle him to anything that any other member of that society is not entitled to. If he acts in a way that doesn't allow members of the society to live in harmony, or he takes un-fair advantage of other members of society, he must expect to be punished just as any other member of society would be pun-ished for those actions. His punishment might take a different form than the punishment someone would receive who is ra-tional but performs immoral acts anyway, but the rules of soci-ety still require that he must lose some of the privileges ex-tended to members in good standing in that society because, if not, then the whole purpose of that society has failed – to allow people to live in harmony without anyone taking unfair advan-tage of anyone else.

ABORTION, SUICIDE, AND EUTHANASIA

Euthanasia and suicide can be evaluated fairly easily, re-garding whether they should be considered right (moral) or wrong (immoral). We simply need to apply the standard rules of society to these actions and look at the results. The standard rules of society, which exist for the purpose of allowing all the members of that society to live together in harmony without anyone taking unfair advantage of anyone else, do not seem to apply to either suicide or euthanasia. Neither of these self-selected, or self-approved, causes of death would be expected to affect the ability of members of society to live together in har-mony, and neither of them would be expected to take unfair ad-vantage of anyone else. Therefore, the standard rules of society that determine morality do not apply here, which means that suicide and euthanasia have no moral component. They are neither morally right nor morally wrong. Someone may object and argue that suicide and euthanasia violate religious doctrines, so they must be morally wrong. It may be true that they violate religious doctrines, but even if every member of a certain society belonged to the same religion, which dictated that suicide and euthanasia are against the law of God, that would still have nothing to do with the morality of suicide and euthanasia or whether they are right or wrong. The reason is because the morality of an act, by definition, can only be determined by whether that act affects the ability of the members of that society to live together in harmony without anyone taking unfair advantage of anyone else. Even if everyone in a society agrees that someone shouldn't commit suicide because, according to religious beliefs, that person will burn in hell if he does, that still does not make it a morally wrong act. It may make it an act that is contrary to the religious principles of all the members of that society, but it is not an act that can be judged as morally right or wrong because it has nothing to do with the standard rules of society.

There are cases one could hypothesize where suicide, for example, could be considered morally wrong, according to the rules of society. For instance, suppose a man decided to commit suicide by jumping off a building, and when he did so, he landed on top of another person and killed him too. According to the rules of society, his action was immoral and wrong because it took unfair advantage of another person in that society by killing him. Or if two partners owned a business that was failing, and one of them committed suicide to get out from under all the debt, leaving his partner owing all the debt instead of just half, then his suicide could be considered immoral, or wrong, because it violates the rules of society that require one to perform no act that takes unfair advantage of someone else. The point is that suicide and euthanasia can only have a moral component attached to them if they affect the ability of the members of society to live together in harmony without anyone taking unfair advantage of anyone else. Actions that are judged to be right or wrong based on religious convictions or other personal beliefs are really just opinions of individuals, based on their stored memories of perceptions and conceptions, and relative to their own frames of reference. They cannot be morally right or wrong unless the actions involve the standard rules of society.

The morality of abortion could be dealt with in the same way as the morality of suicide and euthanasia, if not for the complicating fact that another potential life besides the decision-maker is involved. Before it can be determined whether abortion pertains to the rules of society to decide whether it is morally right or wrong, we first have to determine if the fetus is another member of society or not. If the fetus is a member of society, then abortion is morally wrong because it goes against the rules of society by taking unfair advantage of another member of society. If the fetus is not a member of society, then abortion has nothing to do with the rules of society and cannot be considered morally right or morally wrong.

Is a fetus a person (a member of society)? If it is a person, at what point does it become a person? Religious doctrine presumes that a fetus is a person when God puts a soul in it, but since the concept of a soul is a belief, rather than a fact that can be verified, it can't be used to determine when a fetus becomes a person. The written laws we have state that an abortion can be performed up until somewhere around the twenty-fourth week of pregnancy, which means that the legislators in our society presume a fetus becomes a person at around twenty-four weeks or so after conception. This may be appropriate because if a fetus is removed from its mother's uterus after twenty-four weeks, there is a chance it could survive, whereas, removing the fetus before approximately twenty-four weeks gives it essentially no chance of surviving, even with the intensive care available in a hospital. But then there is the problem that some fetuses may be able to survive outside the uterus at twenty-two weeks, while others may not be able to survive outside the uterus even at twenty-seven weeks after conception. There is no way of knowing for sure whether the fetus could have survived until after the fact, which does not help the case for deciding whether aborting it is morally wrong or not. Rather than choosing an arbitrary period of time during its progressive development, as is done by written law at the present time, an obvious definitive change in the development of the fetus is more appropriate for determining when it becomes a person. That is the only way one can be sure that the fetus either is or is not a person. There are only two times during its development when a fetus has an obvious definitive change where it would be possible to say that before the change it's not a person and after the change it is a person. The first time would be when the egg and sperm fuse to form the single cell that will grow and develop over the next nine months into a baby. The second time would be when the fetus leaves the mother's body and becomes an independently living baby. Any time in between these two events, the fetus is simply in a state of continuous growth and is no more a person one day than the next.

One might think an argument could be made for fertilization of the egg as the time when a new person begins to exist, rather than when the fetus leaves the mother's uterus and becomes a baby, but in actuality, the beginning of the new person (and a new member of society) could only occur after it leaves the mother's uterus, because that is when it becomes conscious for the first time. It can now perceive sensory information voluntarily, form memories of those perceptions, and respond voluntarily. If it is aborted and never has a conscious moment, it has never been a person. Even if a fetus is delivered naturally after nine months, breathes on its own for a short period of time but never gains consciousness, then dies, it cannot be labeled a person, although it is a human being. Until a human being becomes conscious, it is not a person (or a member of society). "Human beings" are defined by their similar genetic material and outward appearance, while "persons" are defined by also being able to voluntarily react with their environment at some time during their lives. In other words, to be a person, one has to have been conscious at some point in his life. All persons are human beings, but not all human beings are persons. Someone might argue this point by positing that if a human being can carry on the basic bodily functions, including breathing on his own, taking nutrition in the form of feeding via tubes, and so on, he is a person, regardless of whether he has ever been conscious. However, the basic bodily functions are all reflexive, and work just like machines, even without continuous input from the brain. For instance, I have cared for patients with verified brain death whose basic bodily functions have continued for three or four days after their brain died. What makes a human being a person is his ability to interact voluntarily with his environment, at least at some time during his life. If he has never interacted voluntarily with his environment, he is as much a person as a rock is. Once a human being becomes conscious, even if only for a short time before lapsing into irreversible coma, he becomes a person, and a member of society.

One argument for abortion being immoral is that it causes pain to the fetus. However, since pain is a perception, and we can only be aware of perceptions while we are conscious, it would be impossible for a fetus to feel pain, in spite of any movements one might observe while stimulating a fetus. For example, an unconscious person will withdraw his foot, and may even form a facial grimace or utter a groan when his foot is vigorously stimulated with a pointed object, but this has nothing to do with the sensation of pain. These are reflexive actions that would occur even if the unconscious person's brain were re-moved from his body. A person *must* be conscious to feel pain. It is that simple. An unconscious person (or fetus) may react to painful stimuli reflexively, but he cannot feel (perceive) pain unless he's conscious. The reason we sometimes have trouble believing this is because when we observe what would normally be perceived as pain when inflicted upon a conscious person being done to an unconscious person, we imagine the pain being inflicted upon ourselves, in our conscious state, so that we can better analyze it in the frame of reference of our own brain. That is, we project what's happening in an unconscious brain onto what's happening in our conscious brain, and the result is a sort of skewed perception. A similar phenomenon occurs while we watch a scary movie. When the killer appears on the screen with a long knife and plunges it into the victim, we cringe and scream because we project this action into our own frame of reference, as if it were happening to us, because our brain can only respond to perceptions that it personally receives and com-pares to memories of similar perceptions. It can't do this unless it perceives the experience as reality, so it "pretends" that the action on the screen is real in order to be able to respond to it.

So now that we've established when a fetus becomes a person, we can make some conclusions about whether abortion is morally wrong or has nothing to do with morality. If the fetus is aborted at any time between conception and spontaneous birth nine months later, and never gains consciousness, then by definition, the abortion is neither moral nor immoral, and cannot be judged as being either morally right or morally wrong. However, if the fetus is removed from the uterus at six months, for instance, and it opens its eyes, begins breathing on its own, and performs actions that are consistent with being conscious, then allowing it to die would be morally wrong. A problem that would be expected to arise is when the mother wants the fetus aborted, but when the physician removes it, he decides, based on his medical knowledge, that with intensive care in the hospital nursery for a few weeks, it is probable that the fetus would develop into a healthy, conscious baby. He mentions this to the mother and she says she does not want anything done for the fetus except to let it die without ever gaining consciousness. What should be done? If the physician honors the mother's request and lets the fetus die without ever gaining consciousness, doing so is neither morally wrong nor morally right because the fetus was never a person. If the physician does not honor the mother's request and puts the fetus in the intensive care unit instead, resulting in a conscious, healthy baby in several weeks, then the physician becomes morally responsible for this new baby, who is now a member of society. (The physician, of course, hopes that the mother will want to keep the baby herself, once she sees it smile at her.)

Someone may wonder if the father of the fetus has any input into deciding whether the fetus should be aborted or not. The answer is that he does. If the mother and father of the fetus cannot agree on whether to have the fetus aborted or not, then having an abortion is morally wrong and not having the abortion is also morally wrong because either way, the rules of society would not be followed. If the mother wanted an abortion and the father did not, and she has the abortion, she would be benefiting at the expense of the father, which the rules of society forbid as being morally wrong. On the other hand, if the mother wanted an abortion and the father did not, and she does not have the abortion, then the father would be benefiting at the expense of the mother, which the rules of society also forbid as being morally wrong. In this case, where the parents can't agree, a compromise must be worked out so that they can ultimately agree on what to do. If a compromise cannot be worked out, and the parents can't agree, then no matter whether the abortion takes place or not, a morally wrong action will have taken place against one of the two parents. However, a seemingly "no-win" situation like this is not insurmountable. One simply performs the morally wrong act that is *least* morally wrong. In this case, the least morally wrong act would be to do what the mother wishes since she is the one who must support the fetus during its development, and therefore is presumed to be the one who will suffer the most if the father's wishes are followed instead of hers.

WHY BE A MORAL PERSON?

From a pragmatic point of view, being a moral person is easier than being an immoral person. When we do the "right" thing, other people like us more, we feel better about ourselves, and we're less prone to feeling anxious or stressed. We all have at least a working knowledge of the standards of morality for our society, and when we do something that is counter to those standards, we are likely to feel the secondary social emotion of guilt. As has been mentioned before, when an emotional memory dictates a response to a perception and it's not heeded, it will continue to send impulses to the response centers of the brain until it is heeded, and those impulses it sends will also trigger the release of stress hormones that can trigger chronic anxiety and other health problems.

Another reason we are likely to act in a moral way is because it usually benefits us more to be moral than immoral, and the brain always chooses the response to a perception that has the most benefit for itself. For instance, if we treat others unfairly, we can then expect them to treat us the same way. The golden rule, which says to treat others as you wish to be treated, did not come about because it is kind and unselfish. It came about because it provides the most benefits, in the long run, for anyone who practices it.

Can an immoral person still treat someone in an ethical manner? The answer is that he can. A person can be immoral, but because he knows it will benefit him most if he treats you ethically, he will do so to achieve the most benefit for himself. For instance, suppose you just got a flat tire while driving down the road, so you pull over to fix it. A man who has been a thief and a robber all his life notices your plight and says he'll fix the tire for you. Since you were on the way to your office when the flat occurred, and you don't want to get your clothes dirty changing the tire, you let him change it for you. After he's finished, he asks if you'd drop him off about two miles up the road on your way to work. You do so and then you never see him again. Even though he is an immoral person, he acted in an ethical manner by changing your tire for you, but he received the benefit of a ride to where he was going two miles up the road.

SUMMARY

Morality and ethics are products of society. They are relative to a particular society and do not exist outside of that society. There are three determiners of morality and ethics. The most important is the standard rules of society, which include anything that promotes members of society living together in harmony without anyone taking unfair advantage of anyone else. Written laws can function as secondary determiners of morality and ethics, as long as they are consistent with the standard rules of society that promote living together in harmony without anyone taking unfair advantage of anyone else. Permanent memories of perceptions and conceptions stored in the brains of the members of society can also function as secondary determiners of morality and ethics, as long as they also are consistent with the standard rules of society.

It is easy to confuse morality and ethics, which are products of society, with the doctrines and principles of religion, which are beliefs of individuals or groups. However, once a person realizes that the rules of society apply to everyone in that society, whether they agree with the rules of society or not, and that the doctrines and principles of religion are beliefs that only apply to the people who believe in the doctrines of that religion, it becomes easier to see why the standard rules of morality and ethics can only apply to a society.

Most of what we have been discussing up until this chapter has placed the individual as the ultimate determiner of what exists, how things are, and what matters. Morality and ethics is the first subject we have discussed that is not determined solely by an individual in his frame of reference. Based on his stored memories of conceptions and perceptions, he may not agree with what the standards for morality in his society dictate are right or wrong, but whether he agrees or not doesn't change whether an act is right or wrong. Only the standard rules of society can determine whether an act is morally or ethically right or wrong.

WHO ARE WE, REALLY?

MOTIVATION

Motivation involves the planning and pursuit of a specific want or need. There are many things that motivate us to act. Some motivators for action originate within the brain itself. The most significant of these are "drives." Other motivators originate outside the brain, in the form of perceptions that we respond to. Whether the motivation is from within the brain or from an external source, every action we take in response to being motivated is accomplished by moving muscles in our body, triggered by impulses from the brain. There is no other way we can respond or act. Everything we have ever done or accomplished is the direct result of our brain sending electric impulses to our muscles, which cause them to move in certain ways. In this chapter we will discuss the various ways we are motivated to act.

WHAT'S IN IT FOR ME?

Our primary motivation is "me first." Any information that is evaluated by the brain for an appropriate action has as its primary goal to benefit that brain (or that person). We always act in the way that benefits our self the most. There are no exceptions to this rule because the brain can only respond to what's going on within itself in its own frame of reference and therefore has no other choice but to act in its own best interest when it evaluates all the information available before choosing the most appropriate action. In order to determine how to react to something, the first thing the brain does in its analysis is to look at how it will be affected –"How does this affect me?" – before initiating the most appropriate response. For instance, going back to an example from an earlier chapter, if I am watching television and an ad comes on that shows the poor, starving children in Africa, then asks for donations to help feed them, my brain perceives this information through my senses of vision and hearing, then compares it to previous similar memories. If the result of this analysis is that I will feel guilty if I don't give money to this cause, then I will donate money – not because I am being altruistic, but because I want to feel good about myself. If the sensory information I see and hear on the television doesn't activate any emotional memories of guilt in my brain, because I've never cared enough about starving people to have ever formed any memories about them, I probably won't pay any attention to the ad, since that's what benefits me the most in that situation.

If it's true that we always act with our own self-interest in mind, then how do we explain fairness and cooperation over seemingly more rational selfishness? The answer is that in the final analysis of most situations, fairness and cooperation actually *are* self-serving. This is because cooperating with others and being fair leads to more peace of mind, less guilt, and less stress in those situations. People who are more likely to practice deferred gratification instead of immediate gratification are also more likely to cooperate with others and be more fair with others because, in the long run, they conceive that it will benefit themselves more.

Oftentimes, when it's not clear what the motivation is for a certain act, it may be because the person performing the act does not have enough information to make a well-informed response. However, his brain still attempts to respond in the way that benefits himself the most, either directly or indirectly.

DRIVES

There are three primary drives that motivate us to act. These are hunger, thirst, and temperature control. Until all three of these drives are satisfied, nearly nothing else matters. Just about everything else that motivates us is for the purpose of improving our mental well being. The three basic drives are all controlled by relatively small, neighboring areas in the deeper parts of the brain that receive constant input from all over the body that they continuously evaluate. If, for example, the center for thirst receives input that the concentration of the blood is becoming too high, it sends signals to other parts of the brain that then cause one to begin searching for something to drink. If the center that controls the temperature of the body senses that the body temperature is beginning to fall below 98.6 degrees Fahrenheit, it sends a signal to the motor area of the brain, which then causes the person to begin shivering to increase the production of heat. The motor area will also cause the person to search for a sweater or jacket to put on in order to conserve heat. These three primary drives are very strong. Although one can occasionally override them for a short period of time, their signals will increase in frequency and strength if ignored. Eventually they will have to be heeded, as long as one is still physically able to do so.

Although the three primary drives are obviously very important for our survival, they are not unique to humans. In fact, all mammals have them, and they function in essentially the same way in all mammals. This is probably because their mechanism of action is so sound and simple that there has never been a need for its modification during the evolution of different species of mammals. Since there is nothing very fascinating about the three basic drives, regarding the human brain, we will move on to the more interesting secondary drives.

Power is the most important secondary drive. In fact, when any of the other secondary drives mentioned in the literature are carefully analyzed, they can usually be determined to be a form of the drive for power. The drive to succeed in business, sports, and other endeavors, as well as the sex drive, are all forms of the drive for power. Other terms that can be used as synonyms for power are "control," "domination," and so on.

What drives a person to seek power? Unlike the case with the three primary drives of hunger, thirst, and temperature control, there is not a particular small area of the brain that is modified for dealing with satisfying the need for power. Power is something that anyone with androgenic hormones, especially testosterone, is driven to seek. The higher the concentration of androgens in the circulation, the stronger the drive is to seek power. The drive for power does not necessarily apply to group interaction, because even if a person were alone in the universe, he would still feel a need to strive for power as long as he had androgenic hormones circulating in his body. Androgenic hormones are also called the "male" hormones, but females have them too. The concentration of androgens in females is usually lower than in males, however.

We are compelled to seek power because an androgenic hormone is released from the gonads, enters the circulation, travels either directly or indirectly to the brain, then triggers specific new electrical activity to occur in certain wires of the brain, which causes the brain to respond by initiating an action related to whatever that particular chemical codes for, including attempts to succeed in business, sports, sex, and other things.

The quest for power continues as long as the androgen level in the circulation warrants it. This is important because it means that even after someone achieves whatever power goal he set out to achieve, he cannot be satisfied with it. That is, he will need to find new levels of power to achieve as long as a certain level of androgens is present in his circulation. For example, a ruler of a country may have a perfect economic health in his country with exports and imports balanced, no poverty or starvation, no unemployment, and all his constituents completely happy. Yet, he cannot be satisfied with this. He must invade other countries in order to satisfy his drive for power. But this is not just something that occurs on a large scale. Even seemingly insignificant things can suffice in the quest for power. We buy more expensive cars than others, we seek richer or more attractive mates than others, we strive to be better at sports than others, we buy bigger houses than others, we work to get the cubicle with the biggest window in it at our office, and so on. Although these are more subtle examples than invading a country, they are still ways we strive to gain power.

The quest for power doesn't have to be recognized as being successful by anyone but the person who seeks it, since it is something that occurs in his brain and his brain is the only frame of reference that matters for determining if he was successful in his attempt at gaining power. For instance, let's say you work in a cubicle in a large office, and the boss just scolded you for making some mistakes on a contract you prepared yesterday. You have lost some power so you decide to get it back by leaving your dirty coffee mug in your cubicle when you go home that night instead of washing it out like you usually do each day before leaving. In your brain, you have regained some power you lost, even though no one else may ever know about your leaving the dirty coffee mug in your cubicle overnight. For purposes of successfully seeking power, it doesn't matter whether anyone else knows or not. All that matters is how you feel about the situation. Leaving the dirty coffee mug overnight may have given you the same feeling of power that the leader of a country felt by invading and conquering another country. Power is relative to the person seeking it.

When someone works at being the center of attention in a gathering of people, this is a more covert attempt at gaining power through control of others' attention. Increasing one's knowledge by reading, taking classes, or listening to experts is also a way of satisfying the need for power. We read in the newspapers about celebrities who become political activists, typically after they have reached the pinnacle of their careers. The reason why this occurs at these specific times is because once one achieves the highest point in a celebrity career goal, there is no more power left to gain in that endeavor, so it must be gained in some other endeavor that is on the same large, attention-gathering scale that one is used to. When internet hackers create havoc in global computer systems, or when teenagers carry guns to school and shoot several people, these actions are the result of the drive for power. They are not socially acceptable ways of seeking power, but they have a twofold benefit for the person performing them – they give immediate gratification and they give the performer of the action a disproportionately large amount of power for the relatively small amount of energy expended. Protestors also seek power through instant gratification rather than by deferred gratification. When we argue, this is to gain control, or power, over the person we are arguing with. Any argument is a form of competition and competition is always a form of power-seeking behavior.

There are some implications of the unquenchable seeking of power that can be disturbing. For instance, the drive for power means that world peace can never be attained, although it might be theoretically easier to attain if women, who generally have lower levels of androgens than men, were the only people who ruled countries. Another example of a problem that results from the constant quest for power is the abuse people inflict on others as a way of gaining power. For instance, a husband, in his personal frame of reference, has the conception that he does not have as much power as he'd like to have, either at work or in his personal goals. In order to gain the power he seeks, he beats his wife. In his mind, this temporarily satisfies his need for power.

There are also some positive results from seeking power. Many of the inventions that have made our lives so much easier are the result of someone seeking power by coming up with something better than what already existed. The invention of the car to replace the horse for transportation and the development of the personal computer are just two of the myriad cases where seeking power results in something positive.

The most important thing about the drive for power is that as long as there are androgens being released into a person's circulation in appropriate concentrations, that person will actively seek to gain what he conceives as power in his frame of reference.

Besides the secondary drive of power, there is another secondary drive initiated by female sex hormones. This is the drive to care for one's offspring. Although the female hormones are usually in higher concentrations in females, they are also found in males to a lesser extent.

EMOTIONS AND MOTIVATION

The way emotions function in our brain's memory system to trigger responses has been discussed in a previous chapter. Without emotions, we would not be able to assign different values to different options. We would always respond to a perception in the most logical way. But the fact that emotional memories are stored with varying degrees of strength and numbers of connections to other wires in the brain makes them all subject to being stronger or weaker than each other, and this is what motivates us to respond so unpredictably to various sensory perceptions. For instance, when I was a five-year-old child, I may have had a very emotionally traumatic experience with another five-year-old child who had curly red hair. Now, every time I see a man with curly red hair, I immediately have an intense dislike for him, even though I may never have met him before. My strongly formed emotional memory of the traumatic event with the curly red-haired child is always activated whenever I see someone with curly red hair, and this memory is so strong that it overpowers any other memories that might also be activated at the same time.

Logical memories are all stored with about the same strength of ability to be recalled, so they are recalled about equally for similar situations, depending on which ones are similar to perceptions and conceptions being evaluated by the brain at a particular time. Because of this, logical memories don't add as much to a person's unique characteristics of motivation as emotional memories do.

Emotions are responsible for giving us our personalities. They are what motivate us to respond more passionately to some perceptions than others, cause us to strive for different goals, and they affect our disposition. We almost never have a thought without some sort of an accompanying emotional component, and these emotional components are what we conceive as giving meaning to our lives. Without emotions, our brain could not assign different values to different options being analyzed within the brain for a response. Our decisions would be logical and flat, similar in nature to how a computer would make decisions.

People who are more emotional and less logical are usually more artistically motivated, while people who are more logical and less emotional tend to be more scientifically motivated.

PAIN AND MOTIVATION

Pain is the strongest motivator for action that exists for us. In fact, when pain signals arrive in the brain, the brain stops everything else it's doing in order to deal with them as quickly as possible so that the pain signals can be stopped. Even the three basic drives of hunger, thirst, and temperature control are put on hold when the brain receives pain signals for evaluation. Although hunger, thirst, and temperature control can eventually lead to our death if they are not attended to, pain usually signifies a more immediate threat to our survival, and that is why it is dealt with immediately, at the expense of anything else that happens to be going on in the brain at that time.

We program large parts of our daily lives around avoiding pain. For instance, we buy certain cars because they are less likely to cause us pain if we are involved in an accident. We pay more money to live in secure areas because we don't want to endure the pain of being shot or stabbed by robbers. Even some of the emotions we experience result from conceptions we have about pain. We feel fear because whatever it is that incites the emotion of fear most likely has pain associated with it. For instance, if I'm hiking through the jungle and a bear suddenly appears in front of me, I experience the emotion of fear because if he bites or mauls me, it's going to hurt. The thought that I might die from this encounter is much less important at that time than the thought that I will experience severe pain.

There are cases on record of people who have been born without the ability to feel pain. These people lead very difficult lives for two reasons. The first is because when one cannot feel pain, he doesn't know when his body is sustaining damage and he therefore does not do anything to stop it. For instance, while sleeping at night, a person who can't feel pain (or discomfort) doesn't turn over in bed to different positions. The result is that the circulation to various extremities can be cut off and he can suffer permanent nerve damage with associated paralysis to the affected limb. The second reason people who can't feel pain have more difficult lives is because they don't possess the normal emotion of fear. Since they don't feel pain, their sense of fear is also markedly reduced or completely absent. It becomes nearly impossible to teach them as children to avoid dangerous situations that usually result in their getting hurt. They have been known to jump off houses, climb trees and then jump out of them, ride their tricycles into walls, and so on.

ENJOYMENT

We all are motivated to enjoy life, but what is it that allows us to enjoy our lives? We want to have enough money to buy whatever we need or desire. We want to be successful at all our endeavors. We want to have plenty of leisure time to spend doing whatever we want to do. We want to be intelligent. Now suppose that we had all the money we wanted so that we could all buy whatever we wanted whenever we wanted without ever having to worry about the money running out. Suppose also that we all knew ahead of time that any endeavor we pursued would be successful, that we all had unlimited time to spend on leisure activities, and that we all knew everything there was to know about everything. Would we all enjoy life? The answer is that we would not. The reason is because it is the *pursuit* of wealth, success, intelligence, and leisure time that we enjoy, not actually having them. This is because the pursuit of these things is actually power-seeking behavior which, after we have satisfied the drives of hunger, thirst, and temperature control, as well as avoided pain, is what motivates us more than anything else. And the drive for power is dynamic rather than static, which means that no matter how successful we are at gaining power, the drive for power demands that we continue to seek more of it. Our enjoyment comes from every small power increase we gain along the way. For instance, banks usually have several vice presidents, all of whom are equal in prominence and all of whom only answer to the president of the bank. Who would derive the most enjoyment from being a vice president of a bank, a person who has been a vice president for the past twenty years or an assistant vice president who was just promoted to vice president of the bank today? The answer is that the new vice president derives the most enjoyment because he has just gained some power. The person who has been a vice president for twenty years has gained no additional power from his job for the past twenty years, so he should be deriving no enjoyment from the long ago achievement of his position as a vice president. Of course, if he still enjoys his same job after twenty years, it probably means he should be fired because the only way he could still enjoy his job after such a long period of time would be if he were still learning new things about it (deriving power from increasing intelligence). If he's still learning new things about his job after twenty years, it probably means that he hasn't paid very close attention to what he does, or that he is in a position that he's under-qualified for. Remember that *change* is what gives meaning to life.

We often hear that life isn't fair, but this is not necessarily true. When referring to reaping the benefits of our labors, life usually delivers what one has earned. If a person is physically and mentally capable of achieving some goal, and he is sufficiently motivated to do so, he can successfully achieve that goal. Those who fail for any other reason than physical or mental capability do so because they are set up to fail. They either are not sufficiently motivated to succeed, they don't have a high enough concentration of androgens in their circulation to drive them along, or they don't have a strong enough emotional input to motivate them to work successfully towards their chosen goal.

Motivation is much stronger for those activities that we think define us. For instance, a mathematician will be much more motivated to prove a difficult theorem before another mathematician proves it than he would be to defeat a professional golfer at a game of golf. What defines us is what we are motivated to try to do better than any other person. In fact, if we each knew what we could excel at, we would be motivated to work at that until we were better at it than anyone else in the world. Statistically, there is at least one thing that each person on earth can do better than any other person on earth. The problem, of course, is finding out what that one thing is.

SUMMARY

All motivation is tailored by the brain to do what benefits us the most. Drives contribute to motivation. There are primary and secondary drives. The primary drives are hunger, thirst, and temperature control. The secondary drives are the quest for power and the care of offspring. Emotions also motivate us to act in specific ways, depending on our unique, stored, emotional memories. Pain is the strongest motivator because it usually signifies an urgent need to correct something that is threatening our survival. What motivates us in our day-to-day activities, after our basic needs are met, is enjoyment. This too, though, depends on the drive for power and the emotions we feel.

WHO ARE WE, REALLY?

SEX – IS IT LOVE?

Two teenagers who have been dating for several months are parked on a dark, deserted road on a Saturday night. The boy turns to the girl and tells her he loves her so much that he wants to take their relationship to the next level by having sex with her, which he refers to as the ultimate act of love. She thinks this is wonderfully romantic and gladly agrees. Within a few days, their relationship has cooled. By the end of the following week, they have broken up. What happened?

In the forty thousand years that have passed since modern man began roaming the earth, it can be stated with certainty that no one has ever initiated the sex act because of "love" for his partner. It has never happened and it never will. In this chapter we will discuss why the term "making love," the synonym for having sex, is an oxymoron rivaled only by "jumbo shrimp."

Love and sex have only been associated since about 1900 or so. Up until about 1600, politics and money were what brought two people together for the purposes of having sex, marrying, and raising children. From about 1600 until 1900, convenience brought people together for these purposes. It wasn't until around 1900 that people began connecting having sex with being in love. That idea became more and more popular over the past hundred years and has grown into what many people mistakenly believe about love and sex today.

SEX

Sex is a drive, and that drive is simply a variation of the drive for power. It is triggered by increased levels of male hormones, especially testosterone, in the circulation. The initiation of sex is always an aggressive act and is always meant to gain power through the person the act is performed on. I use the term "performed on" instead of "performed with" because the sex act is performed to gain power, and power cannot be gained unless domination occurs. It is actually possible for both partners to be aggressive during the sex act because each partner may, in the frame of reference of his own mind, feel he is the one gaining power from the sex act. The power that is sought by the aggressor during the sex act is not necessarily power over, or related to, the sex partner. It can be power that the aggressor feels he needs, in the frame of reference of his own mind, to either boost his lacking self confidence, to renew power that he feels he may have lost during a confrontation with someone else that day, for example, or for a variety of other reasons having nothing to do with the person he initiates the sex act with. The power sought by the aggressor in the sex act can also simply be the result of higher testosterone levels in the circulation for reasons other than a perceived loss of power, since testosterone triggers the desire for power just by its presence in higher than normal concentrations in the blood. That is, testosterone levels can increase after one feels he has lost some power, or the level can increase for many physiological reasons. Psychologically, the person who gains power from the sex act usually does so by inserting something (usually, but not always, a penis) into the sex partner, while the person who is the recipient of this insertion is usually the submissive partner.

In our society, when a male adult entices an underage teenage female to have sex with him, he is arrested and put in jail, which is appropriate because he must be the aggressor and the underage teenage female must be submissive. No one would argue that this amounts to his taking advantage of her. However, it is interesting that when an adult female entices an underage teenage male into having sex with her, the underage teenage male is usually the aggressor during the sex act and the adult female is usually submissive, simply because of the anatomy of the situation. Therefore, it would not be logical to conclude that the adult female took advantage of the underage teenage male, as this would be highly improbable, regardless of their ages, experience, or innocence. Counseling of underage teenagers who have had sex with adults of the opposite sex bears this out. Underage teenage females are much more likely to be traumatized psychologically by having sex with adult males than are underage teenage males who have sex with adult females. In fact, underage teenage males who have had sex with adult females are likely to derive more power over their peers for their sexual "conquest." Rather than feeling embarrassed about it, they are more likely than underage teenage females to brag about it to their peers.

Males are prone to over-represent the number of their sexual conquests, while females are more likely to under-represent theirs because males, who are typically (but not always) the aggressors during the sex act, are the ones who usually gain power from sexual interactions. Males are also four times more likely than females to equate sexual activity with emotional closeness, which means that males tend to think females won't have sex with them unless the females have some positive emotional feelings for them, while females think that males will have sex with them whether the males have any feelings for them or not.

The two teenagers mentioned above who wanted to take their love to the next level by engaging in the "ultimate act of love" drifted apart after having sex because, for the boy, having sex was an aggressive act meant to gain power. Once the act is completed, his quest for power had been achieved and it was time to move on to the next quest for power.

In spite of how they may act, all teenage boys feel quite insecure when interacting with teenage girls. When someone is unsure of himself, it is ultimately due to a lack of power, or one of its synonyms – self-confidence. If a teenage girl will have sex with a teenage boy, this gives the boy more self-confidence. He gains more power each time he has a successful sexual conquest, and feels good about himself – at least for a while, until his increased testosterone and teenage lack of self-confidence cause him to seek more power. He will then seek new teenage girls to have sex with in order to gain more self-confidence and to satisfy his need for power. Being desirable by one teenage girl is not enough to quench his need for power. He must be desirable to all teenage girls in order to satisfy his need for self-confidence, or power. As the teenage boy ages to adulthood, gets a job, gets married, and has children, his self-confidence and testosterone levels should level out. However, if he still goes through periods when he lacks self-confidence, he will probably continue to search for partners who will have sex with him in order to gain his self-confidence (power) back. We occasionally hear about this on the news when it occurs among celebrities and government officials. Even the presidents of our country are not immune to being caught having sex outside of their marriages. One might ask why a president, who has more power than anyone else in the country, would be lacking in self-confidence to the point where he would need to have sex with another person besides his spouse to build up his self-confidence, or feeling of power. The answer is that self-confidence is relative to the frame of reference of the person who feels he lacks it. It doesn't matter what anyone else thinks. All that matters is what that individual conceives in his own brain. For instance, if a child is constantly told by his parents that he is lacking in some quality as he is growing up, he is more likely to have ongoing problems with a lack of self-confidence throughout his entire lifetime, no matter how great his achievements might be judged by other people. Another reason why some people engage in more sexual pursuits is simply because they may have a much higher testosterone level than the average person. If this is the case, they will be more likely to seek more power, which can result in more sexual pursuits with more people when the opportunity presents itself.

One might wonder why the above discussion of sexual pursuit centers on teenage boys instead of teenage girls. The reason is because teenage boys have large increases in the male sex hormones in their circulation during the teenage years, which cause a profound change in power-seeking behavior. Teenage girls don't usually have these profound increases in male sex hormones during their teenage years, so they don't typically engage in dramatically increased power-seeking behavior. Sexual pursuit is only one part of the power-seeking behavior exhibited by teenage boys when they have the usual increase in male sex hormones during the teenage years. They also drive faster in their cars, play their music louder, become more competitive with peers, and perform just about any action that, in their frames of reference, gives them more power, or self-confidence.

As previously mentioned, the desire for sex in both males and females is triggered by the male hormones, especially testosterone. These are the same hormones that trigger the desire for power, domination, and control. When the concentration of the male hormones increases in the circulation system, it triggers electrical impulses in the brain that cause power-seeking behavior. If the person happens to be playing in a sporting event, it will cause him to try harder to defeat his opponents. If the person happens to be a lawyer arguing a case in front of a judge, it may cause him to argue his case more fervently. If the person happens to be at a place where sexual partners might be found, he is more likely to exhibit behavior that is designed for resulting in having sex with them.

Why do we usually seek out sex partners who are attractive? After all, an orgasm isn't going to feel any different whether it's obtained with an attractive partner or an unattractive partner. The reason we search for attractive partners is because that happens to be what everyone else searches for too, making the attractive partners relatively more "unobtainable" than the less attractive sexual partners. So if the attractive sexual partner chooses to have sex with us, this implies that we're also attractive, or desirable. The end result is that we've gained more power by having sex with a desirable sexual partner than an undesirable sexual partner, and since achieving power is the goal when testosterone is released into the circulation, we have maximized the use of the testosterone by finding the most desirable sexual partner. If sex were initiated only for the purpose of experiencing the intense pleasure of an orgasm rather than for gaining power, then we would be less likely to bother finding a sexual partner at all. Masturbation produces orgasmic pleasure that is just as intense as sex with a partner. The difference is that we don't derive the increase in self-confidence, or power, that comes from sex unless we have sex with a partner, and the more desirable that sexual partner is, the more power we gain from the sexual encounter with him. If it were possible for someone to be completely self-confident in everything concerned with his life, and he had no inclination for seeking power, he would not be interested in seeking a sexual partner. He would still want and enjoy the intense pleasure of an orgasm, but it wouldn't matter to him whether his orgasms were the result of masturbation or sex with a partner.

One occasionally hears that the best sex is makeup sex, which occurs after a couple has had an argument. The reason this occurs is because after an argument, both partners have taken a blow to their conception of how much power they each wield in their relationship. Having sex after the argument reestablishes who has the power in the relationship. The person who is more aggressive during the makeup sex gains power, while the person who is more submissive during the makeup sex relinquishes some power. Ideally, both partners will think, in their own frames of reference, that they were each the aggressor who gained power during the makeup sex. This way, both of them will gain power from makeup sex, at least in their own minds, which is all that matters.

LOVE

Love is an emotion, not a drive like sex is. Any resemblance of sex to love is purely coincidental. Since love is an emotion, and emotions are stored memories of intense, or strong, perceptions and conceptions, this means that love simply consists of strongly stored memories. Love is not dependent on circulating chemicals or hormones like the drive for sex is. The feeling of love only exists when the person who is in love either perceives something that activates the memories associated with the object of his love, or when he thinks (forms conceptions) about the person who is the object of his love.

If romantic love consists of strong emotional memories about the person who is the object of that love, then what makes those memories different than the strong emotional memories one might form in relation to friends or family members who are also loved? The difference is twofold. First, other memories associated with the emotional memories of romantic love enhance the emotional memories of romantic love. For instance, if I begin thinking about someone that I have romantic love for, I would not only recall to active memory the strong emotional memories of love, but I would also activate memories that are associated with the smell of her perfume, the way she laughs, the enjoyment of being with her, the feeling of working towards goals that both of us can enjoy, and so on. Second, and most important, the intensity of love is directly proportional to the strength of the stored emotional memories of love the brain has formed that relate to the person who is the object of that love. The stronger the memories are, the stronger the love is. The stored memories of love one has for a friend or family member would simply not be as strongly formed as the memories one has for someone who is the object of romantic love.

There is no such thing as "love at first sight." The reason it can't exist is because it takes time to form all the memories that are related to romantic love and then to store them permanently in the brain. This requires getting to know the person who is the object of that love so that one can experience many perceptions that the brain will store as permanent memories related to that person. As one gets to know the person who is the object of romantic love, the memories related to him become more strongly formed. As the memories become stronger and stronger, they also become more emotional, since emotions are simply strongly formed memories. And when strongly formed memories are recalled to active memory, they initiate strong reactions from the person who recalls them.

When a person first meets someone who might be a potential romantic love interest, the first thing he does is compare his perceptions of that person to stored memories of what his ideal romantic love interest would be like, regarding appearance, wit, self confidence, demeanor, ability for emotional and financial support, and so on. If the perceptions of that person are similar enough to the stored memories of what his ideal love interest would be, then an attempt at continued interaction with that person may be sought. As more information is perceived about the love interest, and it fits more and more with what his ideal love interest would be, the memories related to that person become more strongly formed and hence, more emotional. It is at some point where the memories become stronger, and consequently more emotional, that one realizes that whenever he thinks of that person, he is overwhelmed with emotion. It is then that he realizes he's in love with that person. That is, the memories in his brain that are related to the person who becomes the object of his romantic love become so strongly formed that they not only tend to be recalled to active memory more frequently, meaning he thinks of her all the time, but because they are so strongly formed, when they are recalled to active memory they monopolize a lot of the circuitry of the brain such that his thoughts related to her are much more intense than thoughts associated with routine memories. And because emotional memories have more connections to other areas of the brain, including the areas that release adrenaline for the "fight or flight" response, he feels nervous, has sweaty palms, his heart beats faster, and he has trouble sleeping at night. For example, let's suppose you have a mildly emotional memory for the fear of snakes and a strong emotional memory for the fear of being chased down a dark street by a man waving a machete at you. When you recall these two stored memories into active memory, the one dealing with the man waving the machete, which is much more strongly formed, is much more likely to cause your palms to sweat than the memory of the snakes, because the more strongly formed memory of the man with the machete also has more connections to the area of the brain that stimulates adrenaline to be released. This connection to the adrenaline area is not by accident. It is made because the adrenaline enables you to run away from the man at a faster rate, or gives you more strength to fight him off, if necessary, thus giving you a better chance at survival. The strength of the stored memory is directly related to the intensity of the feeling one gets when it is recalled to active memory because the fact that it is strongly formed also means it has many more connections to other parts of the brain which are also activated when that particular strong memory is activated.

The brain doesn't care whether an intense emotional memory has to do with love, fear, or some other emotion. All it does is respond to the activation of strong memories by preparing us to run or fight by increasing adrenaline. The fact that memories of romantic love happen to be formed as strong emotional memories only confuses the usual mechanisms of response that the brain utilizes when confronted with activated emotional memories, resulting in the sweaty palms and nervousness of romantic love.

The intensity of romantic love lessens with time. The reason for this is that after the strong emotional memories related to love are recalled over and over, eventually the brain pays less attention to them because it is more concerned with evaluating new information than wasting time on reviewing old, repeating information. For instance, one often hears that the way to get rid of a fear is to confront it. What this means is that if a person has a fear of spiders, for example, and he deals with this fear by forcing himself to let a large tarantula crawl up and down his arm, at first it will cause him intense fear. However, after several minutes of letting the spider crawl around on his arm, the brain stops paying attention to the strong emotional memories of fear related to spiders, especially if it perceives nothing earth-shattering happening when the spider crawls on his arm. Eventually, the memories related to the fear of spiders are allowed to weaken to the point where, when a spider is seen, the person no longer can recall the strong emotional memory for fear of spiders. In a similar fashion, after the strong memories of romantic love with a certain person are recalled over and over for comparison to the perceptions and conceptions that triggered them, and nothing earth-shattering occurs that requires immediate attention, eventually their strength will decrease and they won't be as strongly emotional when perceptions and conceptions dealing with the loved one are analyzed by the brain. Love does not necessarily disappear in these cases. What happens is that the two people who are in love have settled into a routine where they know what each other will do in specific situations and act accordingly. They have become such a part of each other's lives that they can operate as a unit, stabilizing their partnership even more, because there are fewer "surprises" about each other that they have to be ready to deal with. Of course, in some cases, the strength of the emotional memories decreases significantly before a partnership bond forms and then, as the memories that were strongly emotional become relatively weak routine memories, the two people drift apart as a result.

Sex is erroneously associated with love because both are very personal and intimate. That is where the similarity ends, however. One of the attributes of romantic love is that it has a stabilizing influence on our lives. Two people who are truly in love work to help each other so that the partnership can flourish. On the other hand, sex is never stabilizing because it is an act that always requires at least one partner to be aggressive. The aggressive sex partner always seeks to gain power, usually at the expense of the submissive sex partner, during the sex act. The submissive partner may submit to the aggressive partner out of love for that partner, but that does not mean the sex act is an act of love. Cuddling and doing things for each other, for example, would more resemble acts of love.

People who tend to be more emotional are more likely to fall in love faster and more often than people who are relatively less emotional. This is simply because the circuitry in the brains of people who are more emotional is set up to more easily form stronger memories of various experiences, or perceptions, including those perceptions involving a potential love interest.

When someone is in love, he has a strong desire to have his love returned by the person he is in love with. In fact, nearly 80 percent of both males and females say that knowing the person they love loves them back is more important than having sex with that person. The reason why it is so important to have our love returned goes back to the fact that we always do what benefits ourselves the most. There are no exceptions to this rule. When we have a very strong emotional attachment to someone, we don't want that person to "get away," because the stronger the emotional attachment, the more we need to interact with that person. If that person loves us back, they are much less likely to leave us.

It has been suggested that dopamine, a neurotransmitter, might be responsible for the desire to have our love returned by the person we are in love with, but this will not turn out to be the case because dopamine varies in concentration frequently and is quite ubiquitous whether someone is in love or not. This fact doesn't square well, logically, with dopamine having anything to do with causing someone to want his love returned.

Since love is an emotion and sex is a drive that is unrelated to emotion, having sex with someone requires no emotional involvement with that person. In other words, one doesn't even have to like a person in order to have sex with him. Taking this a step further, people often have sex with partners that they *dislike*, as long as they can be the aggressors. In their frames of reference, having sex with people they dislike while being the aggressor gives them a feeling of power over those sex partners. This practice is not as uncommon as one might think. Males, especially, also frequently fantasize about having sex with someone they dislike when they are having sex with their usual sex partners because it makes them feel more empowered, especially when sex with their usual partner becomes more routine, predictable, and consequently, less power-producing.

When a person has an orgasm, the brain releases oxytocin in females and vasopressin in males. Some people feel that these two chemicals are associated with a feeling of attachment, ultimately linking sex and love together. However, this is not the case for two reasons. Oxytocin and vasopressin have not been shown convincingly to be related to attachment in humans because they are not released from the brain in high enough concentrations at orgasm to accurately predict anything they may do. Second, they are released in the same concentrations from the brain when orgasm is reached via masturbation, and masturbation does not result in a feeling of attachment.

MYTHS ABOUT LOVE AND SEX

We probably get most of our information about love and sex from watching movies and television. Unfortunately, the writers for most of the shows that deal with love and sex are untrained in that field and write their shows to be more interesting than true to life. Any resemblance between movie drama and what really occurs in life is usually lacking. For instance, I was watching a drama recently and heard one actor say to another that sex is the most sincere expression of love. As has been discussed, nothing could be further from the truth.

There are a few myths about love and sex that have been making the rounds over the years. It is time to dispel them.

Myth #1 – "Romantic love and sex are related because the combination of the two leads to producing offspring, then staying together long enough to raise them." This is untrue for at least two reasons. First, we've already shown that love and sex are not related because sex is a drive initiated as a quest for power and love is an emotion that consists of stored memories in the brain. Second, it has only been since about 1900 that people married and raised children because they were in love. Up until then, people had sex and raised their offspring because of convenience, prominence of their ancestors, or for political reasons.

Myth #2 – "Falling in love stimulates the sex drive." Falling in love does not affect the sex drive. The sex drive is stimulated by male hormones in the circulation and falling in love occurs because of the increase in the strength of stored memories related to the object of a person's love. Although there have been some proposals that various neurotransmitters can cross-stimulate both the sex drive and the emotion of love, this has never been proven to be the case, and probably never will.

Myth #3 – "Romantic love is an addiction." It is impossible to be addicted to memories, no matter how strongly formed they are. All one can do with memories is recall them and make some kind of a response to them. Some people may associate love with addiction because addictions can also trigger the release of adrenaline that causes insomnia, sweaty palms, and nervousness when someone is withdrawing from various addictive drugs, giving the same outward appearance as the nervousness and sweaty palms a person in love gets when he is with the person he loves. But the release of adrenaline in these two situations is for entirely different reasons.

SUMMARY

In answer to the question posed by the title of this chapter, sex is not love. Sex is a subset of the drive for power, while romantic love is a set of very strongly formed emotional memories about the object of a person's love. Sex and love have only been associated together for the past hundred years or so, probably because they both involve intimate relationships.

RELIGION

Religion has been around for as long as human beings have been roaming the earth. It has taken every form imaginable, from worshiping animals to making human sacrifices, but the one thing all the different forms of religion have in common is that they offer hope that something else is waiting for us after we die.

Unlike every other animal on earth, we know that we are going to eventually die. Knowing that our lives are limited can be very depressing because no matter what we accomplish while we're here on earth, it will mean nothing to us after we die. But if our death is really just a transfer to another form of life, then what we do while alive on earth can "carry over" to our continued existence in the next life. Religion not only offers the hope that our lives have meaning, but that they will continue on for eternity.

Religion serves another purpose too. It tempers our actions. Many people who would not be inclined to act fairly while interacting with other people will do so anyway because they fear that if they don't treat others fairly, they will pay for it after they die. In this case, fear of punishment after we die is a strong motivator to treat others in the way we would want to be treated.

THE BRAIN AND RELIGION

In the brain, religion consists of stored memories of perceptions we have experienced as well as conceptions of beliefs we have formed based on perceptions. When new perceptions related to religion are experienced, they are compared to our stored memories related to religion, and if a response is indicated, then the brain will direct what that response should be. Since everyone has memories about religion that are unique to his own brain, everyone has at least a slightly different frame of reference for his religious beliefs than everyone else. For instance, suppose I was raised in a home where religion figured prominently in my day-to-day activities. When I was ten years old, I may have decided to steal some money from my mother's purse to buy candy. If, after I took the money and went to the store, I ran into some bullies at the store who beat me up and took my money, I might then think that this was God's way of punishing me for stealing the money. I would form new memories of the perception of being beat up by the bullies, of the conception that God was punishing me because I stole the money, and combinations of these perceptions and conceptions, all of which would be recalled each time the opportunity to steal some money presented itself. These memories would all be associated with religion memories in my brain and they would be unique to my brain because no one else would have had the exact same experience that caused them to be formed just like they were formed in my brain. In my frame of reference, stealing money would be conceived as something that is not wise to do because one will ultimately end up worse off after God punishes him in some way for stealing.

Memories associated with religion that are formed in our brain when we are children can affect our thought processes for the rest of our lives. When our parents tell us that we will "burn in hell" if we do something morally wrong, we form strong emotional memories of these perceptions as children because they are associated with fear. These memories are not easily forgotten as we become adults, and they often are recalled from our stored memories for comparison to form a response when perceptions occur that might tempt us to do something wrong, even after we become adults. These strong emotional memories then dictate a response that keeps us from doing things that would be considered wrong. Without a religious background, there would be no memories relating to punishment in the after-life for doing the wrong thing and we would be less inclined to act appropriately. Some people think that it is absolutely essential to teach religion to children, even if their parents are not believers, because it not only gives the children hope that their lives will have meaning, but also because it sets their course so that they are a positive influence on society instead of a negative influence. It can be compared to the concepts of Santa Claus and the Easter Bunny. That is, these mythical characters give the children something to look forward to in the hope of gaining some kind of reward for being good. Once they are old enough to realize that these characters don't exist, they have already formed the memories associated with hope, and these memories will likely remain stored in their brain in some conceptual form throughout their lives. Likewise with religion, once the memories are formed during childhood that dictate concepts of hope and doing what's fair in dealings with others, these memories are likely to remain stored in children's brains as they live their lives, even after they are old enough to form their own ideas about whether God exists for them or not. In other words, if a person forms memories related to religion that cause him to do what's right because he will be punished after he dies if he doesn't, or for other religious reasons, then, even if he becomes an atheist in his adult life, he may still use those stored memories to guide him into doing what's right in spite of not believing in God or an afterlife.

Experiments have been performed using the transcranial magnetic stimulator (TMS) that was mentioned in Part I. By stimulating various parts of the brain through different areas of the scalp, patients can be made to believe they are sensing the presence of a supernatural being, such as a guardian angel, the devil, Mary, the mother of God, and others. The conclusions that researchers have drawn from these experiments are that spiritual experiences are nothing more than a product of our brain. But there is nothing really phenomenal or surprising about this because we've already established that everything that exists for every individual is exactly what his own brain determines to exist for him in his own frame of reference, based on new perceptions and memories of previous perceptions and conceptions. So, of course spiritual experiences are a product of the brain – just as everything else is. If you experience (perceive) it, then it exists for you.

Suppose you and I are standing on a street corner and suddenly you see God standing in front of you. If you start talking to Him and He answers you, then He exists for you in your frame of reference. If you reach out to touch Him and you feel His robes or the texture of His hand, no one can deny that you truly interacted with God. The fact that I am standing right beside you on the same street corner and did not see or feel God has absolutely nothing to do with your experience with God. For me, He did not exist on the street corner. For you, He did exist on that street corner. I can try to prove that He wasn't really there, but I would be no more successful at doing this than you would be at trying to prove to me that He was there. If I told you that He didn't exist there because I could put my hand where you said He was standing and I didn't feel anything, you could equally say that He does exist there because you could put your hand there where He is standing and feel His hand or touch His clothes. As long as we are both being truthful and honest with our statements about the presence of God on that street corner, then for you, He truly did exist there, and for me, He truly did not exist there. Whether there were fifty people also standing on the street corner who agree with me that He wasn't there, or whether there were fifty people also standing there who agreed with you that He was there, that would have nothing to do with what is true for you and what is true for me. You truly saw God and I truly did not see Him. Like many other concepts we've been discussing, the beliefs and experiences related to religion are strictly individual. What exists depends entirely on what each individual perceives or conceives with his own brain in his own frame of reference. The reason why there is so much controversy associated with subjects like this is because we want everyone else to see things our way (in order for us to gain more self confidence, or power, ultimately). That is impossible though, because no two people have the same stored memories to use when evaluating new perceptions.

One of the problems that makes it difficult to accept that someone might have seen God standing before him while others didn't is that we tend to assume that since most people don't usually see God standing before them, then chances are that the person who says he sees God and touches His hand or His clothes is just looking for attention or is psychologically impaired, since this often turns out to be the case once the person who claims to have seen God is questioned rigorously. But if someone truly believes that he has perceived God, then in his frame of reference, he has truly seen God, and there is no way to prove that he did not because there is no way to get inside the frame of reference of someone else's brain to determine exactly what is happening in his frame of reference. Of course, if someone truly believed that he had actually seen God, we would expect that person's life to change dramatically. For instance, now that he knows for sure that there is an afterlife to be lived with God, we would guess that he would never do anything contrary to what his religious doctrine teaches for fear of being damned in the afterlife. If we saw him acting contrary to the way a person who had seen God would act, we could reasonably deduce that his claim of seeing God was a hoax. No one would be foolish enough to do things forbidden by his religious doctrines if he knew for sure that God existed. This scenario is played out frequently by evangelists who preach in front of huge audiences on television or other large venues. They often claim to "know God personally," yet they are caught doing things that are forbidden by the doctrines of their religion, such as committing adultery, stealing money from their congregations, and so on. In these cases, it would appear that their claims of personally knowing God are hoaxes. If one truly believes that he perceives God, then for him, God is reality and no other brain can have more "authority" to say he's wrong, nor can a "majority" of people have the authority to say he is wrong. What each person perceives as reality is what actually exists as reality for that person. There is no "standard reality" that everyone's perceptions can be compared to in order to determine what is "really" true. There is no "really true" because no one's reality is any less real than anyone else's.

There are tests such as fMRI and PET scanning that can be performed on the brain to show what part of the brain becomes active when, for example, a person thinks about God. Although it is possible to tell what part of the brain deals with thoughts about God, it is not possible to tell from the activity seen in those areas whether the person truly is seeing God or is imagining it. Only the person himself can determine whether the perception of God is real or imagined. There is no way for anyone else to prove it except indirectly by observing how a person's actions and the way he lives his life change after he claims to have seen God.

People who are "born-again Christians" necessarily have a more difficult time convincing others that they have actually changed their personalities from being immoral to being moral. This is because all the memories dealing with morality that have been stored in their brain throughout their entire life have to be reprogrammed so that instead of comparing those old memories to new perceptions they experience, and then making their usual immoral response, they now will cause the brain to dictate a moral response instead. This is incredibly difficult to do because it requires de-programming all the immoral memories out of the brain, then reprogramming them with moral memories that can be used to compare with new, incoming perceptions dealing with moral issues. It requires an enormous amount of concentration, patience, and re-analyzation of situations involving morality so that the moral choice can be made as the most appropriate response by that person's brain. It is much easier to claim to be a born-again Christian in order to receive more tolerance and acceptance by others while still acting in the same manner as previously. This is where actions become more important than verbal claims for determining whether someone is being honest about his conversion from an immoral to a moral person. For instance, I saw a football player give an interview on television a few years ago in which he claimed to have put aside all his immoral ways and was now a born-again Christian who would only act in a moral way from then on. A few weeks later I read that he had been arrested for physically abusing his girlfriend. His verbal claims did not match up with his actions, giving little credence to his claims of changing from an immoral to a moral person.

LOGIC AND RELIGION

When one tries to prove the existence or non-existence of God using logic, he is doomed to failure. For almost all of us, religion is based on belief, not proof. (The exception would be those few people who, in their own frame of reference, truly have seen and spoken with God.) Trying to apply logic to prove the existence of God will fail because the mystique and the purpose of religion is in requiring us to believe something that can't be proven. If it could be proven, it would no longer be religion; it would be fact. This has not stopped theologians from trying to logically prove that God exists, and it has not stopped atheists from trying to logically prove that God does not exist.

For instance, those who are opposed to the existence of religion state that if God is a perfect being, then He is incapable of deceiving human beings and He is incapable of imperfection, which means that He would have had to make us perfect as well. If we are perfect, then we can't do anything that is considered to be morally wrong. Since we often do things that are morally wrong, this is offered as proof that God can't exist. One of the problems with this logic is that it supposes there is a universal standard for morality that applies to all people in all societies, which is not the case. Each society has its own standard rules that dictate what is morally right and morally wrong in that particular society, so there can't be a moral standard that applies to everyone in every society. Further, there is no standard for what denotes perfection. Perfection is a concept that means different things to different people, and no one's idea of perfection is any more valid than anyone else's. Finally, why does God have to be "perfect," and even if He is perfect, why does that mean that He had to create us perfect too? There's no logical reason why God has to be perfect or why we had to be made perfect if He is responsible for creating us, other than that someone claimed it had to be so.

Religion teaches us that God did many wonderful things for us when He made us. In fact, the underlying message that one usually obtains from religious teachings is that everything God does centers on us. We would have to be very egotistical to think this way, though. As large as the universe is, it would make more logical sense that we are just one small, nearly insignificant part of all the activities God has on his calendar. We pray to God to give us a promotion at work, or we pray to God to help us win a sporting event, but when we think about these things, what we are really asking God to do is favor us and to slight one of our co-workers so that we can benefit from a promotion instead of him. Or we are asking God to make the other team lose so our team can win, thus favoring us over them. If we truly thought that God might listen to us and grant our request, then, according to the standard rules of our particular society, we would be acting in an immoral manner. That is, we would be taking unfair advantage of someone else so that we could prosper. Logically, then, by praying to God for something, we could be acting in an immoral manner.

Many people try to live their lives according to the writings in the Bible, but the Bible was not written until several hundred years after the events that are recorded in it actually took place. This means that for several hundred years, those events were handed down from one generation to the next by word of mouth. Most of us have played the parlor game where we whisper a sentence to a person, then that person whispers it to the next person, and so on, until the message has been passed along to ten or fifteen people. When the last person receives the message, he says it out loud. The sentence he repeats usually bears little resemblance to the original sentence. If this can happen over the course of a few minutes, passing information through ten to fifteen people, one can only imagine what happens to information that gets passed verbally from generation to generation for several hundred years. The chances that what is recorded in the Bible is what actually occurred are logically improbable.

As long as religion remains something that we believe in for the purposes of making our lives more meaningful and for helping us to treat others more fairly, it will serve its purpose much better than if we try to logically prove whether God does or does not exist. There is no way to prove whether God exists. Any attempts to prove His existence or non-existence can always be easily refuted.

SUMMARY

Religion offers hope that there is something more in store for us than our lives here on earth. It also tempers our actions so that we have an incentive to treat others fairly. Our stored memories that relate to religion determine our feelings about religion.

Some people claim to have actually been in the presence of God and no one can directly prove that they have not been in His presence. However, observing their actions can give a good indication of whether they truly believe they have been in God's presence or if it is a hoax.

It is not possible to prove that God exists by using logic, because the premise of religion is "belief," not perception via our five senses.

SOCIETY

How would it feel to be the only human being on earth? We've often heard that because we are a social species, we require interaction with other people in order to thrive. We've been around other people since we were infants so we don't really have anything to compare our socialization to. There have been many isolation experiments performed in labs and these generally show that people don't deal well on a psychological basis with being deprived of contact with other people. The problem with these experiments, though, is that they are biased. The people used for the experiments have always had associations with other people, so removing them from this environment would naturally cause some anxiety, just as changing anyone's usual routine would cause some anxiety. But if one were the only human on earth, and had never met another human, would he be anxious about having no contact with other people? He probably would not. He would seek to satisfy his drives for hunger, thirst, and maintenance of body temperature, but since he had never had contact with another human being, socialization would be unnecessary for his contentment. Soci-

335

ety is what results when more than one person exist and interact with each other. In this chapter, we will look at the peculiarities that are created by the existence of a society.

RULES OF SOCIETY

In order for a society to exist, there has to be a set of rules that everyone must follow to remain in good standing in that society. If there were no rules, then a society could not exist. What would exist is a state of nature where everyone would be free to do whatever he wanted without having to worry about treating anyone fairly.

For an ideal society to exist, some essential rules are necessary. There would need to be a ruling group of people, and this group could not profit any more by their decisions than the non-ruling members of society. There would need to be a group to enforce the rules, because this would deter people from breaking the rules. If they did break the rules, this group would separate them out to protect the rest of society from them. The rules would have to apply equally to everyone. Everyone would have to have an equal opportunity to pursue any goals they wished, with no member of the society being more favored than any other. Goals would have a known value based on the difficulty and time required to achieve them. A rocket scientist would command more respect and more monetary reward than a dishwasher in a restaurant, for example. Finally, there would need to be standards by which everyone could determine where he fit into various aspects of society. For instance, the terms "normal" and "abnormal," "stupid" and "smart," "attractive" and "unattractive," and so on, are only applicable in a society. This has nothing to do with each person's own concept of his qualities, as each person chooses these for himself, based on his stored memories in his own frame of reference. But regardless of what each individual's reality is in his frame of reference, there would need to be standards applied to all the members of the society. For instance, suppose someone feels, in his own frame of reference, that he is qualified to fly a jetliner loaded with several hundred people, even though he's never taken a flying lesson. The standards of society would prevent him from getting in a plane and attempting to fly it because those standards dictate that he must have a pilot's license and show some level of expertise in flying before he is allowed to put hundreds of other people at risk by trying to fly the plane. A society requires its members to assume responsibility for their actions within that society. Responsibility is a product of society and only exists when a society exists. It does not exist outside of a society.

The essential rules mentioned above could be eliminated if we knew for sure that everyone within a society would follow three basic rules, which would include treating others as we wish to be treated, not taking anything we haven't earned, and not taking more than we can use, even if we've earned it. Even though a large majority of people living in a society might follow these rules, *everyone* must follow them in order for a society to function smoothly.

How important is each human life in a society? The purpose of forming a society is to protect its members as they live their lives, so this indicates that a human life is considered to be very important by the society. As a single entity, a human life is not so important, but as an individual representative of a society, it is extremely important because each human life signifies the entire society and everything it stands for. That is, the whole purpose of a society is to make life easier for its members who are in good standing, and if it doesn't protect or value one member in good standing, then in theory, it's not inclined to protect or value any other members in good standing. For instance, suppose I'm a used car salesman, and I tell you that every car on my lot is in perfect condition and ready to go. You look at all my cars and decide that you like one of them. You get in to test drive it and it won't start. Since that car wasn't in perfect condition and ready to go, your logical assumption is that the rest of my cars are probably faulty too. Similarly, if a society doesn't do everything it can to protect one member in good standing, everyone else in that society can logically assume that it won't do everything it can to protect anyone else either, and the society will necessarily fail.

INDIVIDUALS IN SOCIETY

It may seem ironic that the success of a society depends on everyone working together so that no one takes unfair advantage of anyone else. This is ironic because no one ever does anything "for the good of society." Our brain is structured so that its primary purpose is to benefit the person it belongs to. The reason why a society works at all, given that it is made up of individuals whose only purpose is to do what benefits themselves the most is because working together with other members of society *is* what benefits each individual the most, in the long run. For instance, it's a lot easier to agree to give up some of my freedom to do whatever I want, and instead let the law enforcement agencies protect me from being robbed, than it would be to have to defend myself against others every time I went

outside my home. It is also a lot easier doing a job I enjoy doing in order to earn money to buy food than having to worry
about growing my own food. So living in a society does not
contradict the fact that everyone only acts in his own best interest.

"The fairest system is the one that benefits me the most."
We can each make this claim. For instance, people who like
being around other people do so because their brain conceives
that they are receiving more benefit from those people than they
are giving to them. People who don't like being around other
people conceive that they are receiving less benefit from the association than they are having to give. As an example, suppose
there are two celebrities who have just come upon a group of
people in a public place. The first celebrity stops and talks with
the people, signs autographs, and truly enjoys interacting with
them. The second celebrity wishes he could turn around and
run the other way because he doesn't want to talk with the people or sign autographs for them. He truly does not like interacting with them. What causes such a difference between these
two celebrities? Remember that everyone only chooses a response that they feel will benefit themselves the most. In the
first case, the celebrity enjoys signing autographs and interacting with the people because he may have a self-esteem problem.
Having people make him the center of attention improves his
self-esteem, so he is more than happy to interact with them.
Using his time to interact with the people benefits him the most.
In the second case, the celebrity already has enough self-
confidence that he doesn't have to be the center of attention to
improve it. Interacting with the people wastes his time and
benefits him less than if he avoided the crowd. Both celebrities

acted in completely opposite ways, yet both of them did exactly what benefited themselves the most.

No one ever makes a choice or performs an act that he doesn't perceive will affect him either directly or indirectly. When a "good Samaritan" takes time to help someone he doesn't know, he derives a benefit from this that, if nothing else, allows him to feel better about himself after helping the person than he would have felt if he had passed the person by. If he were not going to derive more benefit from helping the person than ignoring him, his brain would not allow him to help out. This is why some people will help out a person in need and others won't, in spite of the fact that they are all part of the same society.

We are all exactly where we want to be in life, based on the way we have made decisions throughout our lives. This may sound strange when one thinks of people who are living in poverty with little to eat, but remember that every decision we make is what we conceive will benefit us the most. There is no other way our brain can act. So every decision that got a person to where he is right now was made by him with his best interest in mind, based on the stored memories of perceptions and conceptions in his brain. Someone who is more educated should have a broader fund of memories to draw from before making a response to a perception or conception, so that his benefit is more optimized than someone who is making responses with a narrower fund of memories. If someone living in severe poverty is given fifty dollars to buy food for himself and his family, and he goes to the local convenience store and buys fifty dollars worth of lottery tickets instead, it is because his brain has decided that this is the best use of that money. He figures that if he wins the lottery, he will never have to worry about where he will get the next fifty dollars after he spends the fifty dollars he just got to buy food. Someone else with a broader fund of memories will figure out that the chances of winning the lottery are essentially zero, so it would make more sense to buy food for his family with the fifty dollars he's just received instead of buying lottery tickets with the money. All the responses made by an individual are the ones that his brain has determined will benefit him the most. For instance, obesity is a major concern for most people in our society at the present time. In interviews conducted on television, one can hear people lament that they have tried everything to lose weight but nothing works. In analyzing this situation, all one has to remember is that the brain only chooses as a response what it thinks will benefit that person the most. In this case, the enjoyment from the taste of the food or the psychological benefit derived from eating food to excess outweighs the benefit his brain predicts would result from becoming slim. The result is that the person does what his brain predicts will benefit him the most. When the benefit of being slim outweighs the benefit derived from eating to excess, then the person will lose weight. For example, I once had a patient who had been trying to lose thirty pounds for over five years, but had been completely unsuccessful. Finally, after he suspected that his wife was starting to see another man, he lost the thirty pounds over a period of two months. In his case, the thought of the major change of losing his wife because he thought he was no longer attractive to her caused his brain to choose avoiding excess eating because now a greater benefit for him would result from losing weight and keeping his wife than from the enjoyment he received by eating tasty foods. Losing the weight did not make any difference in the outcome of his marital problems, but the important point is that in his brain, in his frame of reference, he thought it would, which is all that matters when one determines what will benefit himself the most.

When we choose as individuals living in a society, we choose for everyone else in that society to make the same choice in the same situation. This is because everyone in our society is considered equal to everyone else and no one's life is any more important than anyone else's. Although this sounds like a logical and simple plan, it seems to be very difficult to follow. We can all think of examples of people who do things that they certainly wouldn't want everyone else to do, like cutting in front of people in queue lines, throwing trash out of car windows, not telling a clerk if he gave back too much change from a transaction, taking towels and other items from motels, and so on.

BREAKING THE RULES

Is it ever okay to break the rules of society? Even as far back as a few thousand years ago, there was a group of people called "sophists" who claimed that the laws of societies were not natural and unchangeable, but were merely the product of custom or convention. The more radical sophists argued that no one was obliged to obey any laws except when it was advantageous to do so. It is suspected that the sophists were referring to "local" laws enacted by the officials of the towns and cities rather than the standard rules of society, because local laws are proposed and enacted to benefit one group at the expense of another, while the standard rules of society, which only dictate that no one should do anything that interferes with everyone in

that society living together in harmony with no one taking unfair advantage of anyone else, are meant to benefit everyone at
the unfair expense of no one. And remember that only the standard rules of society apply to morality. Local rules and laws
don't necessarily have anything to do with morality. For instance, if the speed limit on a certain road is twenty-five miles
per hour, and you happen to have quick reflexes, such that you
feel very comfortable driving forty-five miles per hour on that
particular road, there is nothing morally wrong with your driving over the speed limit at forty-five miles per hour. Local rules
and laws are made for everyone, and so they are necessarily
compromises that benefit some at the expense of others. A
ninety year old man driving faster than twenty-five miles per
hour on the road in question may be endangering anyone's life
who happens to be on that road because his reflexes are not
good enough to deal with speeds faster than twenty-five miles
per hour in that area.

Laws are usually made to protect the members of society
from the most extreme behaviors, but since an average of only
ten percent of people fall within the extreme in any given situation, this means that ninety percent of the members of society
derive no benefit from local laws. If they disobey the local laws
and are not caught, there is nothing immoral or wrong with doing so. The exception, of course, would be when a local law
crosses over into the realm of the standard rules of society. For
instance, if a local law states that it is illegal to dump toxic
waste in a river, and someone dumps toxic waste in the river
anyway, then he would not only be breaking the local law, but
would also be breaking the standard rules of society which state
that no one can take unfair advantage of anyone else. By

dumping the toxic waste in the river, one would be taking unfair advantage of others by potentially poisoning them, and this would be an immoral act because it is breaking the standard rules of society.

It is never okay to break the standard rules of society because they always exist for the benefit of everyone who is a member in good standing in that society and are always associated with morality. It is sometimes okay to break the local rules and laws, however, because they usually exist to benefit some people at the expense of others and are not necessarily associated with morality.

RIGHTS

When we use the term "rights," we are usually referring to something that we deserve, either because we've earned it or because it is bestowed upon all members of a particular society. For instance, if I worked forty hours last week at the local fast food franchise for seven dollars per hour, I have earned a right to two hundred and eighty dollars of my employer's money. If I am a member of a society that guarantees all its members the freedom to say what they want, then I have a right to speak freely because of my membership in that society. Notice that rights involve interactions between at least two people. This means that rights refer to treatment of individuals by other individuals. If a person became shipwrecked on a deserted island, and he was the only one there, the term "rights" would be meaningless. We can take the application of rights a step further and say that rights are a product of society and that they only apply to people living within a particular society. That is, rights are created by a society and exist only as long as that society exists.

Our constitution says that we are "endowed by our Creator with certain inalienable rights," and it mentions that some of these are "life, liberty, and the pursuit of happiness." Nobody knows for sure whether our Creator endowed us with any inalienable rights, so this statement cannot possibly be correct. A correct statement would have been that the *constitution* gives us certain rights, including life, liberty, and the pursuit of happiness, because the constitution is what defines our society and only a society can bestow rights upon its members. There are no "natural," or "God-given," rights that we could ever be aware of. Even life, liberty, and the pursuit of happiness are not natural rights. For instance, one could easily imagine living in a society that did not allow personal liberty, such as occurs in some communist societies. In these societies, there is no right to liberty. Liberty is a right that is granted by a society, not by nature. In a state of nature, where society doesn't exist, it's "every man for himself," and the term "rights" is meaningless.

How far do the rights granted by a society extend? We hear people say that everyone in our society has the right to medical care, for example. But is this really true? The answer is that it is not. No one ever has a right to the services of another just by being a member of a particular society unless slavery is an accepted condition of that society. Since slavery was abolished in our society a long time ago, bestowing members of our society with a "right" to medical care would be forbidden because it would require people working in the medical field to provide medical care to anyone who wanted it, even if the medical care personnel preferred not to provide that care. If they were forced to provide medical care anyway, regardless of circumstances or payment for services, that would be equivalent to slavery.

Are there any rights that can't be taken away? Since rights are granted by society to members living in that society, any of them can also be taken away by society. We do this all the time in our society when we incarcerate criminals for breaking the laws. They lose their right to liberty when they are locked in a prison cell. If liberty were an "inalienable" right granted by one's Creator, then it would be forbidden by society to incarcerate criminals because it would be depriving them of an inalienable right of liberty that would be outside the jurisdiction of society. But since liberty is a right bestowed by society, then society can also decide to take that right away when the rules of society are broken.

THE NATURE OF SOCIETY

We know that there are standard rules of society that dictate what is moral and what isn't. We also know that there are rights associated with being a member of society. What we haven=t discussed is how a society, with all its members, functions.

One of the first things that stands out about any society is its tendency towards achieving conformity, because conformity is what allows a society to prosper and thrive. There is a middle ground of "standards" and "normals" when referring to intelligence, appearance, achievements, and so on, that every successful society attempts to have all its members achieve. The reason for this is because the people who are able to benefit a society the most are those who fall in the middle of any group. For instance, the people with average intelligence, holding average jobs, and who are average in every other way are the ones who maintain the society. In our society, that includes the members of the middle class. They pay the bulk of the taxes, they don't individually wield enough power to create situations that have the potential to negatively affect the society like the rich class can, and they don't drain the assets of the society by using the free goods and services available like the poor class does. As long as a society has about seventy percent of its members falling near the center between two extremes for any aspect that is graded in that society, it will have a tendency to thrive. That is, if one draws a graph that plots some aspect of a society on the x-axis and the number of members who exhibit that aspect on the y-axis, and this results in a distinctly formed bell-shaped curve, that society will thrive. But once the bell-shaped curve starts becoming skewed in one direction or the other, this means the society is beginning to have problems. For instance, in our society, it is being said that the middle class is shrinking while the poor class is growing, meaning that the amount of money being paid for taxes is also shrinking while the use of free goods and services available is increasing. As a result of this phenomenon, there have been some questions about whether social security will go broke for lack of funds over the next several years if this trend continues. Even in non-democratic societies, the fate of the society depends on most of its members tending towards being average in all aspects of that society.

Societies rely on "group mentality" for conformity within that society. People who think or act differently than the majority tend to be ostracized. For instance, people tend to favor certain artistic accomplishments because the artists are already noteworthy or because others favor them, rather than because the art appeals to their personal sense of beauty. Most of the members of a society must necessarily be followers in order for that society to thrive. The followers rely on the leaders to tell them what to do and how to think. The followers say, "give me a chance" while the leaders say, "I'll make my own chance." It may sound somewhat depressing that most of us are destined to be followers, but if the majority of the members of a society were leaders, no one would be likely to listen to anyone else and chaos would result.

Originally, way back on our evolutionary tree, we were not programmed to be part of a society. We were each programmed to be independently living beings. This is obvious because of the way our brain is formed such that it always chooses what benefits itself the most, and can only be aware of what goes on within itself, not what goes on in any other brain. So living in a society goes against our "program," but we do it because it allows us not only a better chance of surviving, but also a better chance of being happier and more content than if we lived in a state of nature. Our underlying thought while living in a society to gain these benefits is that if we are willing to give up living in a state of nature, where we are free to do whatever we want whenever we want, in order to derive the benefits of living in a society, then we expect everyone else to do the same in that society too. And if they don't, they either need to be punished or we need to withdraw from that society. We might then join another society because ours is not treating us in the same way we are treating it.

In general, any person who asks for concessions from another person, group, or society is rendered subservient to that person, group, or society.

One of the inherent, potential problems with any society is the "ten percent" rule. That is, in any given situation, approximately ten percent of the members are responsible for ninety percent of whatever is being measured. For instance, in our society, ten percent of the people control ninety percent of the wealth; ten percent of the people use ninety percent of the healthcare dollars; ten percent of the people are responsible for ninety percent of the crime; ten percent of the people make daily decisions that affect ninety percent of the population; ten percent of the people produce ninety percent of the food; and so on.

How does war fit with a society? The quickest way to obtain change is to wage war. A society is set up to benefit all its members if they agree to give up some of the freedoms they would have in a state of nature, so war might be waged if something that society feels it needs is found to be lacking, in which case that society will wage war to get it from another society if a buy-and-sell compromise can't be worked out. (Another reason for waging war, as mentioned in a previous chapter, would be the need for power, which has already been discussed.) Wars among different societies are inevitable because changing needs is inevitable. The only way to prevent wars between different societies might be to unite the entire world population into one vast society.

THE FUTURE OF SOCIETY

Any society needs to change as conditions within that society change. For instance, when our society was first formed in the 1700s, there were relatively few people who were members of it. There was encouragement to have large families to strengthen the position of our society through manufacturing and the production of more goods and services. Over the past hundred years or so, the population has grown to the point where people are now encouraged not to have so many children in order to prevent overpopulation and a depletion of resources. With the advent of home computers, our society is changing from one whose members were more active to one whose members are less active as they spend more time sitting at a computer terminal. This has resulted in significant problems with both childhood and adult obesity, which will require society to gradually change further to deal with this newer problem.

As things change in a society, values change as well. If the population of a society becomes larger and larger, to the point where there is not enough food to feed everyone, the value of a human life will necessarily decrease. The population in our society was growing in an exponential fashion until just a few decades ago when it started becoming obvious that if we continued reproducing at that rate, it wouldn't be long before we would be unable to sustain our society.

Although an ideal society strives to have its members fall into the middle categories in all aspects of that society, diversity is also necessary in order to allow self-sufficiency of that society. If everyone in a particular society had the same intelligence, the same memories, the same skills, and the same goals, that society would quickly fail because nothing could be accomplished.

In our society, the fact that we have evolved with a trait for compassion will eventually cause significant problems because compassion is detrimental to the survival of a society. We feel sympathy for those who are unable to fend for themselves. We are also quick to donate money, time, and resources such as food and water to members of society who need these things, even though logic and the ultimate health of society dictates that survival of the fittest is what sustains a constantly evolving society. In the long run, however, the pendulum will swing the other way. That is, as limited resources are eventually depleted, there will be a forced and more dramatic survival of the fittest. The number of those who survive will be much smaller, but they may be better equipped, genetically, to reestablish a healthy society.

At the beginning of this chapter, it was mentioned that if a society doesn't do everything it can to protect one member, everyone else in that society can logically assume that it won't do everything it can to protect anyone else either, and the society will necessarily fail. This seems to be in direct disagreement with what was just stated about compassion leading to the ultimate downfall of a society, but it really isn't because this statement applies to members of a society who are in "good standing" in that society. Compassion is detrimental to the survival of a society when it leads to taking care of those members who are not in good standing in that society, either because they are not willing, or because they are not able, to contribute something to that society. That is, they are technically not members in good standing in the society because they are taking unfair advantage of the compassionate members. The fact that they might be unable to take care of themselves has nothing to do with it. If they are receiving something from someone else without reciprocating in any way, then they are not abiding by the standard rules of society, which dictate that everyone live together in harmony with no one taking unfair advantage of anyone else. Therefore, they are not members in good standing in that society.

If society is not able to reestablish itself after a cataclysmic reorganization following a critical shortage of needed resources, then it will disappear. If the destruction of resources is large enough, more and more groups of animals will also disappear, starting with the animals that are higher on the food chain. Eventually, just insects will be left, then bacteria, then, as more nutrients become available, the whole cycle will start over with more and more complex animals evolving again over millions of years by mutations of the genetic material.

SUMMARY

We are all programmed to live in a state of nature, but we give up some of our freedoms to live in society because it is more conducive to our ultimate survival. The standard rules of society are such that they allow members of society to live together in harmony without anyone taking unfair advantage of anyone else. Society strives for conformity because that is what allows it to thrive. At the present time, in the midst of our evolution, we seem to have developed a mutation in our genetic makeup that causes us to have compassion for others. Eventually, this will cause problems for the survival of our society as it interferes with "survival of the fittest," and prevents our species from evolving.

SELECTED BIBLIOGRAPHY

(This list includes sources of information that are in book form, readily available to readers who may be interested in learning more about a particular subject. It does not include journal articles used in researching information for this book.)

- Asimov, Isaac. *Atom - Journey Across the Subatomic Cosmos*. New York: Truman Talley/Plume, 1992.
- Asimov, Isaac. *Understanding Physics*. Barnes & Noble, 1966.
- Bennett, Deborah J. *Logic Made Easy*. New York: W. W. Norton, 2004.
- Blatner, David. *The Joy of Pi*. Walker Publishing, 1997.
- Born, Rainer, (ed.). *Artificial Intelligence*. London: Croom, Helm, 1987.
- Campbell, Don G. *Introduction to the Musical Brain*. Magnamusic-Baton, 1983.
- Carpenter, Malcolm. *Core Text of Neuroanatomy*. Baltimore: Williams & Wilkins, 1991.
- Cole, K. C. *The Universe and the Teacup*. New York: Harcourt Brace, 1998.
- Copi, Irving M. and Cohen, Carl. *Introduction to Logic*. New Jersey: Prentice Hall, 2002.
- Damer, T. Edward. *Attacking Faulty Reasoning*. Wadsworth/Thomson Learning, 2001.
- Davies, Paul. *About Time*. New York: Touchstone, 1995.
- Dunham, William. *The Mathematical Universe*. New York, John Wiley & Sons, 1994.
- Eastaway, Rob, and Wyndham, Jeremy. *Why Do Buses Come in Threes?* New York, John Wiley & Sons, 1998.
- Einstein, Albert. *The Meaning of Relativity*. New Jersey: Princeton University Press, 1922.
- Feynman, Richard. *Six Easy Pieces*. Reading, Massachusetts: Perseus, 1963.
- Fisher, Helen. *Why We Love*. New York: Henry Holt, 2004.
- Gribbin, John. *Schrodinger=s Kittens and the Search for Reality*. Boston: Back Bay, 1995.
- Hawking, Stephen. *The Universe in a Nutshell*. New York: Bantam, 2001.
- Hawking, Stephen, and Penrose, Roger. *The Nature of Space and Time*. New Jersey: Princeton University Press, 1996.
- Hawkins, Jeff, and Blakeslee, Sandra. *On Intelligence*. New York: Times Books, 2004.
- Johnson, Steven. *Mind Wide Open*. New York: Scribner, 2004.
- Kandel, Eric; Schwartz, James; Jessell, Thomas. *Principles of Neural Science*. New York: McGraw Hill, 2000.
- Kaku, Michio. *Beyond Einstein*. New York: Anchor Books, 1995.
- Kaku, Michio. *Hyperspace*. New York: Anchor Books, 1994.
- Laughlin, Robert. *A Different Universe*. New York: Basic Books, 2005.
- Lavine, T. Z. *From Socrates to Sartre*. New York: Bantam, 1984.
- LeDoux, Joseph. *Synaptic Self*. New York: Penquin, 2002.
- Lerner, Eric. *The Big Bang Never Happened*. New York: Vintage, 1991.
- Livio, Mario. *The Golden Ratio*. New York: Broadway Books, 2002.
- Maor, Eli. *e: The Story of a Number*. Princeton: Princeton University Press, 1994.
- Oh, Shin. *Clinical Electromyography*. Baltimore: Williams & Wilkins, 1994.
- Penrose, Roger. *The Large, the Small and the Human Mind*. Cambridge: Cambridge University Press, 1997.

SELECTED BIBLIOGRAPHY

- Popkin, Richard, and Stroll, Avrum. *Philosophy Made Simple.* New York: Double-day, 1993.
- Rothman, Tony. *Instant Physics.* New York: Fawcett Columbine, 1995.
- Satinover, Jeffrey. *The Quantum Brain.* New York: John Wiley & Sons, 2001.
- Seife, Charles. *Zero - The Biography of a Dangerous Idea.* New York: Penquin, 2000.
- Shermer, Michael. *The Science of Good and Evil.* New York: Times Books, 2004.
- Smolin, Lee. *Three Roads to Quantum Gravity.* New York: Basic Books, 2001.
- Smoot, George, and Davidson, Keay. *Wrinkles in Time.* New York: Avon, 1993.
- Stevens, Charles. *The Six Core Theories of Modern Physics.* Cambridge: MIT Press, 1995.
- Victor, Maurice; Ropper, Allan. *Adams and Victor's Principles of Neurology.* New York: McGraw Hill, 2001.
- Wolf, Fred. *Parallel Universes.* New York: Touchstone, 1988.
- Wolfson, Richard. *Simply Einstein.* New York: W. W. Norton & Co, 2003.
- Zukav, Gary. *The Dancing Wu Li Masters.* New York: Bantam, 1979.

INDEX